HIDDEN HEROES

HIDDEN HEROES

THE ROLE OF PHYSICIANS IN SPORTS

UDIT DAVE

NEW DEGREE PRESS

HIDDEN HEROES

The Role of Physicians in Sports

ISBN   978-1-64137-244-2   *Paperback*

         978-1-64137-245-9   *Ebook*

Dedicated to my late grandfather and inspiration, Dr. Bharat J. Pandya.

We love you and miss you Dadaji.

CONTENTS

INTRODUCTION

———

It's common: A football player taking a huge hit and taking an extra-long time to get up, like Adrian Peterson. A basketball player goes up to finish at the rim and then crumples to the floor, gripping their leg, like Paul George. A baseball player takes a pitch to the face and falls to the dirt, like Giancarlo Stanton. Major injuries are relatively ubiquitous in sports, whether it's a weekend warrior getting hurt during a recreation league game or a professional athlete having their season cut unexpectedly short.

Thankfully, what is equally prevalent is seeing athletes come back from injuries as if they never even occurred in the first place. Athletes are frequently able to bounce back from major injuries and return to their respective sports performing as well as if not better than they had prior to getting hurt. An immense amount of physical and mental effort goes into an athlete's recovery from a major injury, and athletes would be unable to bounce back from injuries the way they do without their unrelenting dedication. However, the crucial role of physicians in bringing about these seemingly miraculous recoveries goes largely unheralded. Countless times, physicians have extended, revived, and revitalized the careers of elite athletes through complex surgeries and precise rehabilitation regimens.

Behind all the monster contracts and deep community roots that compose the limelight of sports, physicians are consistently there, ensuring the greatest athletes in the world are receiving the exceptional care they deserve. This book will provide incredible stories about some of the most surprising sports comebacks, innovative approaches to catastrophic injuries, and the role of physicians as a critical puzzle piece to keeping athletes on top of their game. This includes exploring how Dr. James Andrews saved Drew Brees' dislocated throwing shoulder and helped him break the NFL passing record and bring a Super Bowl to New Orleans in the aftermath of Hurricane Katrina, how LeBron James' medical team has helped him remain one of the most durable athletes of all time and a contender for title of greatest athlete of all time, how doctors helped transform Stephen Curry from an undersized, injury-prone guard to most the prolific shooter in NBA history, and how Adrian Peterson was able to shatter all expectations and redefine what it means to successfully return from a torn ACL.

I have grown up falling in love with sports. I'm a die-hard New York Knicks, Yankees, and Jets fan. I spend a lot of my free time outside on the basketball court with my friends or inside, huddled around a TV watching whatever game is on. I also hope to attend medical school to serve as an advocate for patients and have an important role in caring for and healing patients. Through speaking through a multitude of superstar athletes and world-class physicians, I have garnered an appreciation for the power of medicine in sports and the ways it enables athletes to continue to improve. This book will take you behind the scenes of the injuries and subsequent recoveries of your favorite athletes and will illuminate their path from doubtful recovery to unforgettable redemption in the form of championships and Hall of Fame careers. You will get an insight into the lives of the athletes and the doctors who treat them, the science behind the injuries, the way the injury was treated, how the athletes recovered, and why their stories are important. So if you are someone who is interested in medicine, sports, or the intersections between them, dive right in and learn about these hidden heroes.

CHAPTER 1

STEPHEN CURRY: ALWAYS TAKE THE 3

———

"He was turning his ankle in completely nontraditional, crazy ways," Warriors general manager Bob Myers said.[1]

Today it seems like a distant memory, but for two-time MVP Stephen Curry, there was a growing consensus early in his career that injuries would keep him from achieving his potential.

---

1   Curry, Stephen, and Neymar Jr. "The Crossover." The Players' Tribune. Last modified October 30, 2018. Accessed May 29, 2019. https://www.theplayerstribune.com/en-us/articles/the-crossover-stephen-curry-neymar-jr.

"It was scary," Myers continued. "I'd never seen someone sprain his ankle like that prior to Steph. And I haven't seen it since."[2]

As a former superstar athlete at Davidson College who did not have trouble with his right ankle prior to getting drafted by the Warriors, Curry's frustration was evident.

"People started saying, 'Steph's got glass ankles. Steph's Grant Hill 2.0,'" Davidson teammate and one of Curry's closest friends Bryant Barr said. "He didn't hide his emotions, his frustration, for anyone."[3]

"Some analysts felt in 2012 that Curry's contract extension was a risk for the Warriors due to his history of ankle injuries, as Curry played in just 26 games in his third season," USA Today reporter Nick Schwartz wrote.[4]

But just how did medical science turn a player with "glass ankles" into a two-time MVP?

For many purists, Steph Curry and his peers have ruined the game of basketball.

---

2   Ibid

3   Ibid

4   Schwartz, Nick. "Steph Curry reflects on what draft experts said about him in 2009." FTW! Last modified January 9, 2019. https://ftw.usatoday.com/2019/01/steph-curry-draft-criticism-warriors.

My grandfather was not one of those purists.

"Take the 3! You're open enough, always take the extra point! Always take the 3!"

I was five years old at this point, sitting right next to my grandpa in my parents' bedroom, playing NBA Live 2003 on the PlayStation 2. This was the first video game I had ever played, and I had gotten good enough to the point where my grandpa would sometimes opt to watch me play instead of watching old Indian movies on TV.

With my grandpa egging me on, I would dribble up the court and pull up for a 3-pointer almost every single time, and he loved to see it.

My grandpa permanently moved to New York a few years after my mom and dad had in the late 1980s. He had fallen in love with the hard-nosed basketball of the early 1990s, but as was usually the case with my grandpa, he was way ahead of his time. He was obsessed with the 3-pointer when he first started watching basketball seriously in 1995, a season in which only 5.9 3-pointers were attempted per game by NBA teams, compared to the 32 threes teams attempted in 2019.[5]

5 "NBA League Averages - Per Game." Basketball Reference. Last modified 2019. Accessed May 29, 2019. https://www.basketball-reference.com/leagues/NBA_stats_per_game.html.

He loved 3-pointers as much as he hated missed free throws, and every time he saw the Knicks miss a crucial free throw and go on to lose the game, which happened pretty frequently in the early 2000s, he'd turn to me and say, "If I was the coach, I would fine them a million dollars for every free throw they missed! How do you miss? There isn't even anyone in front of you!" Although the Knicks had some decent years once Carmelo Anthony became the leader of the team, they never won anything meaningful and continued to disappoint.

My grandfather's love of basketball began to wane, but not due to any changes in the sport or how it was played. He was diagnosed with Parkinson's and began spending more and more time in his room at my house whenever he would stay with us for a few weeks.

Steph Curry changed that.

Curry was everything my grandpa had dreamed of seeing in a basketball player: He rarely missed free throws and he always took the 3. Whenever I went over to his room and asked if he wanted to come watch basketball with my parents and me, my grandpa would always make what had now started to feel like a long trek over to the family room if the Warriors were playing.

On February 27, 2016, after helping my grandpa walk over to the family room, we watched the Warriors take on the

Thunder. Curry was having a solid game when, with a little over 10 minutes left in the 3rd quarter, he stumbled on a fast break drive to the hoop. Replays showed Thunder guard Russell Westbrook leaping and landing on the side of Curry's foot. Curry's ankle twisted sharply as he fell, and his back collided with the stanchion. As the Thunder took the ball the other way, Curry yelled across the court to his teammates to foul to stop the action so that he could be pulled out of the game. As he hobbled off the court and into the locker room, grimacing, the Thunder's arena was filled with a buzz of murmurs.[6] Steph Curry had notoriously bad ankles, and seeing the only unanimous NBA MVP ever gingerly walk off the court with the Thunder nursing a mere 5-point lead made it look like this game was now the Thunder's to lose.

After walking off the court with what appeared to be a serious ankle injury, Steph Curry limped back to the court just 5 minutes later.

As he rejoined his team on the court, my grandpa's eyes lit up and he sat up on the sofa just as it had begun to look like he was going to fall asleep. Curry began to hit acrobatic 3 after acrobatic 3, my grandpa was fully engaged. Steph Curry had

---

6   "THE GAME Steph Curry BECAME a LEGEND 2016.02.27 at Thunder - 46 Pts, 12 3's, CLUTCH!" Video file. YouTube. Posted by FreeDawkins, February 27, 2016. Accessed May 29, 2019. https://www. youtube.com/watch?v=quI--kovXgI.

made him fall in love with the game of basketball all over again, and it was beautiful to watch.

As Curry crossed over what seemed like a hundred times before burying a 3 from 30 feet away with two defenders in his face, it was evident that my grandpa was enjoying basketball more than he had since Michael Jordan's prime.

As the game went into overtime, Curry hit his 10th 3-pointer of the game, breaking his own NBA record for most 3-pointers in a season. His next trip up the floor, he crossed the ball between his legs and then quickly behind his back and rose up behind the 3-point line, contorting his body sideways to get a shot up over the taller Kyle Singler. As Curry hit the floor, his 11th 3 of the night sank effortlessly, tying the game up with about two and a half minutes left.

As the seconds wound down, Curry continued to score points at the free-throw line, putting the Warriors on his back and singlehandedly keeping them in the contest. With a little under 10 seconds remaining, Russell Westbrook leaned towards the basket and tried to bank a shot in off the glass. As the shot careened off the backboard and the rim and Warriors forward Andre Iguodala snatched the rebound with just over 6 seconds remaining, everyone's eyes darted to Steph Curry, who motioned for the ball with his hands.

As Curry brought it up the floor, he stopped right at the edge of the Thunder logo between the half-court line and the 3-point line and pulled up. Curry had been hitting deep 3s all day, but as this one went up, I stood up and yelled "no way!" As the shot went up, the Thunder turned around to look at the hoop and time stood still as the fans fell dead silent with the fate of their team dependent on this one Hail Mary shot from 35 feet out. As the shot fell in off the back iron of the rim, the crowd screamed in agony as announcer Mike Breen yelled, "BANG! BANG! Oh, what a SHOT from Curry!" As Curry ran into the back court and started his patented shimmying, my grandpa looked like a little kid again, staring at the TV screen a little longer. With that shot, Curry had tied the record for 3-pointers in a single NBA game, with 12.[7] As he watched the Warriors walk off the court victorious, my grandpa just shook his head and said, "Wow!" Honestly, no one could have said they saw this coming.

Steph Curry's meteoric rise to back-to-back MVP awards and undeniable status as the greatest shooter to ever play the game was seen as a near impossibility a few seasons ago, when Steph was known for having the worst ankles in the NBA.

---

7   "THE GAME Steph Curry BECAME a LEGEND 2016.02.27 at Thunder - 46 Pts, 12 3's, CLUTCH!" Video file. YouTube. Posted by FreeDawkins, February 27, 2016. Accessed May 29, 2019. https://www.youtube.com/watch?v=quI--kovXgI.

But what happened?

After Steph Curry's second NBA season, which was plagued
by ankle sprains that forced him to miss eight games, he
underwent surgery on his right ankle at OrthoCarolina
Sports Medicine Center in Charlotte, N.C., in May 2011.[8]
Dr. Bob Anderson, a foot and ankle specialist, rebuilt two
ligaments in Curry's ankle that had become stretched out of
shape due to his past injuries and were contributing to ankle
sprains he had been experiencing.[9]

The procedure was meant to strengthen Curry's ankles and
improve their stability on the basketball court. However, in
the 2012 season following the procedure, Curry sprained his
ankle five more times and played in only 26 of 82 regular
season games.[10]

After the 2012 season, Curry opted to have another procedure done on his troublesome ankle. In April 2012, Curry

---

8   "Warriors Guard Stephen Curry Undergoes Successful Surgery on
    Right Ankle." NBA.com. Last modified May 25, 2011. Accessed May
    29, 2019. https://www.nba.com/warriors/news/curry_ankle_sur-
    gery_052511.html.

9   Torre, Pablo S. "How Stephen Curry got the best worst ankles in
    sports play." ESPN. Last modified February 10, 2016. Accessed May
    29, 2019. http://www.espn.com/nba/story/_/id/14750602/how-gold-
    en-state-warriors-stephen-curry-got-best-worst-ankles-sports.

10 "Stephen Curry." Basketball Reference. Last modified 2019. Accessed
    May 29, 2019. https://www.basketball-reference.com/players/c/cur-
    rysto1.html.

had a right ankle procedure performed on him at Southern California Orthopedic Institute by Dr. Richard Ferkel, who had operated on hundreds of NBA players before Curry.[11]

Prior to Curry's operation, the source of his ankle issues had not been successfully pinpointed despite the use of a vast array of tests, from MRIs, x-rays, and CAT scans to nerve tests and strength tests. However, while Curry was under anesthesia and unable to feel pain, Dr. Ferkel conducted stress x-rays on him. Stress x-rays are collected and examined after the area of the body in question has been physically strained. After Curry's stress x-rays indicated that he did not have any structural damage to his ankle ligaments, Dr. Ferkel inserted a small camera into Curry's subtalar and ankle joints, which revealed significant scar tissue, bone spurs, cartilage chips, and general inflammation.[12]

Dr. Ferkel recalled that the inside of Curry's ankle "looked like crab meat. It was good news. The least intrusive outcome." Dr. Ferkel then cleaned up the debris and damaged tissue in Curry's ankle with a medical motorized shaver and vacuum – a process that took less than an hour and a half.[13]

---

11 Torre, Pablo S. "How Stephen Curry got the best worst ankles in sports play." ESPN. Last modified February 10, 2016. Accessed May 29, 2019. http://www.espn.com/nba/story/_/id/14750602/

12 Ibid

13 Ibid

Curry was projected to return to the court within three to four months. But the months ahead would prove to take a toll on Curry that was both physical and mental.

After he had the second ankle surgery, Steph was sitting with his wife, Ayesha, in his home in Charlotte. He recalled, "In that moment it really tested my mental strength to get through the dog days of a second summer of rehab and not really know where the end was going to be. You always wonder, again like what we just talked about it–you're chasing greatness, you want to be great, but the one thing I couldn't control was my health, in terms of my ankles. And [Ayesha] gave me that one line of like, 'Don't forget who you are.' That kind of kept me focused on that mission."[14]

Three months into his rehab process, Curry told Brandon Payne, his personal trainer, "I feel like I've been doing nothing but rehabbing for two years. I feel like I'm never going to be able to play again."[15]

14 Curry, Stephen, and Neymar Jr. "The Crossover." The Players' Tribune. Last modified October 30, 2018. Accessed May 29, 2019.https://www.theplayerstribune.com/en-us/articles/the-crossover-stephen-curry-neymar-jr.

15 Torre, Pablo S. "How Stephen Curry got the best worst ankles in sports play." ESPN. Last modified February 10, 2016. Accessed May 29, 2019. http://www.espn.com/nba/story/_/id/14750602/

Warriors general manager Bob Myers said, "Steph was sick and tired of it. He said, 'this ankle thing is not going to be my life.'"[16]

Steph Curry's game is predicated around being able to switch directions quickly and efficiently, which allows him to get to the rim and finish or step outside and create space to hit a 3.

According to Keke Lyles, who was hired as the Warriors' performance director in 2013, Curry could maintain his quickness and mobility while reducing the load on his ankles. In fact, Lyles claimed, "Shiftiness is an ankle strategy, but power comes from the hips. We wanted to teach Steph how to load his hips to help unload his ankles."[17]

As Curry continued to face ankle issues and even sprained his ankle in the 2013 playoffs, he remembered, "I had to do rehab in between games; it brought back memories."[18] As Curry was eager to strengthen his ankles so these injuries would be few and far between, he and Lyles went to work.

"Steph's central nervous system is the best I've worked with. It's why he's a great golfer, a great bowler, a great shooter," Lyles recalls.

---

16 Ibid
17 Ibid
18 Ibid

As he worked with Lyles and Payne, Curry learned the single-leg hip airplane, a yoga pose he utilized to develop his core strength and balance. He also began working on the hip hinge, which is used in lower-body exercises to build explosion. Curry worked on his glutes and hamstrings with trap-bar deadlifts. As he continued to work with Lyles, Curry became a true gym rat. He went from deadlifting 200 pounds to clearing 400 pounds with ease.[19]

According to teammate and fellow "Splash Brother" Klay Thompson, "The man was always in the gym. Steph just stuck with the routine. He works on his body as much as he works on his jump shot.[20]

Steph's father, former NBA star Dell Curry, recalled, "Steph became more aware of how he needs to take care of his body. It helped him understand that his body is his career."[21]

Lyles and Payne continued to help Curry work on his core strength with one-legged workouts. Payne had Curry do single-leg reverse lunges, single-leg deadlifts, and rear-foot elevated single-leg squats. Payne even had Curry work with flashing strobe goggles on, which disrupted his vision and

---

19 Ibid
20 Torre, Pablo S. "How Stephen Curry got the best worst ankles in sports play." ESPN. Last modified February 10, 2016. Accessed May 29, 2019. http://www.espn.com/nba/story/_/id/14750602/
21 Ibid

made him focus on proprioception – the awareness of his body in space.[22]

According to the personal trainer, "Steph's core strength is second to none."

Once a potentially elite talent dreading a long, taxing recovery process, with the help of his doctors and training staff, Curry has transformed into a training addict.[23]

According to Warriors assistant general manager Kirk Lacob, "The way Steph moves, 98% of the world would hurt themselves trying to run like that. I think people would pay to watch Steph work out. The ankle thing made him work smarter, to counteract him ever being put in that position again."[24] While Curry's injury risks posed a threat to the Warriors, according to Bob Meyers, the Warriors' eventually fortuitous gamble on him made perfect sense.

Meyers proclaimed, "We bet on who he is as a human being. We bet on his ability. We bet on the fact that he was the type of player who'd do everything within his power to come back and be smart and be diligent."[25] Curry went so far as

---

22 Ibid
23 Ibid
24 Ibid
25 Ibid

to say that his ankle injury is responsible for molding him into the once-in-a-generation player he is today, claiming "It definitely drove home my work ethic. Post-surgery, it's kept me driven about taking advantage of every day. There was a time when I was just worried about playing basketball, much less playing at a high level. Now I try to have as much fun out there as possible. You don't enjoy the surgery and the rehab process. But I enjoy how I came out of it, for sure."[26]

"I wanted to be great because I saw greatness ahead of me," Steph recalls.[27] As he looked back on his comeback from two major ankle surgeries to winning three NBA titles and two MVP awards, Steph said, "And two years later, or almost three years later, I'm back on the court, winning the championship. So that moment right there was kind of like the lowest of lows, and it was kind of only up from there…. And that's what makes it all work."[28]

As Stephen Curry continues to propel the Golden State Warriors as the cornerstone of perhaps the greatest dynasty in NBA history, the role of his trainers and medical team in allowing him to continue his hall-of-fame career proves to be invaluable. As Curry continues to heed his doctors'

---

26 Ibid

27 Curry, Stephen, and Neymar Jr. "The Crossover." The Players' Tribune. Last modified October 30, 2018. Accessed May 29, 2019. https://www.theplayerstribune.com/en-us

28 Ibid

and trainers' advice by working on his core and lower body strength while taking special care of his ankle, he evidently has also been heeding the advice my grandpa would give me as I played video games.

Steph always takes the 3.

And he usually makes it.

CHAPTER 2

KEVIN DURANT: PASSING THE TORCH

———

As we gathered around the TV in my friend Nihar's basement, most of us were filled with hope. Nihar wanted the Warriors to continue their streak of dominance against undermatched opponents such as the Cavaliers in the 2017 NBA Finals, which we had gathered to watch. Some of my friends, like Ashwin, Raj, Nisarg, Ayush, and Brandon, didn't feel too strongly about the result of the game, but showed up to watch the game and spend time with people they only got to hang out with for a couple of months out of the year. My friend Milan, citing an irrational hatred of LeBron James and an understandable disdain for the Golden State Warriors, just wanted to enjoy the endless slices of pizza and hopefully watch a competitive game. Jibran, a basketball purist and a historian of the game, wanted nothing less than a battle for the ages. Then there were the rest of us – Ansh, Ajay, and I – the die-hard LeBron James fans who had grown up looking up to him and had fallen in love with the game of basketball through watching him take over the NBA.

We continued to pass around the Papa John's pies loaded with different assortments of vegetables, and it felt wonderful. Most of us had known each other since the sixth grade, others for even longer. Despite going our separate ways for college and picking up new endeavors when we were back for summers, one thing was a given: we would always be together to watch the NBA Finals. Ansh, Ajay, and I were sitting at one end of a long, winding couch, each of us wearing a different colorway of a LeBron James t-shirt and caring less about whether we got the pizza topped with jalapeños and pineapples and more about whether LeBron could find a way to win against a team that was the modern-day, real-life equivalent of the Monstars from Space Jam. As the Warriors started to pull away at the end of the first quarter, Ansh got up and said, "it's over, Warriors in 4." As he sat down, visibly frustrated, he added, "And Udit got tricked, the moron spent five extra dollars to get the NBA Finals edition of the LeBron shirt."

The Warriors and Cavaliers were neck-and-neck as this pivotal Game Three was beginning to wind down, and we were on the edge of our seats. As Cavaliers sharpshooter

Kyle Korver missed a corner three, Warriors superstar Kevin Durant, affectionately known by the basketball world as KD, rose up to grab the rebound off of the rim. With a little over 50 seconds remaining and the Cavaliers leading 113 to 111, the Warriors were in dire need of a bucket. As Durant calmly brought it up the floor, the Cavaliers transitioned to playing defense, with James stepping up to guard Durant. With no hesitation, Durant dribbled up to the three-point line and pulled up for the shot. With the hand of the 6'8" LeBron James in his face, Durant easily got the shot off and it splashed through the net, taking the air out of the stunned Cleveland crowd in a now nearly silent, motionless Quicken Loans Arena. As Cavs point guard Kyrie Irving took the inbound pass and pushed the ball the other way, KD looked out to the crowd and snarled, relishing his role as the villain.[29] Hell broke loose in Nihar's basement. Everyone was irate, yelling at Nihar to wipe the smirk off of his face. "LeBron sucks," sighed Ajay, visibly deflated by Durant's dagger. As Irving clanged a shot off the rim, it was becoming clear that this game was over. It was becoming clear that this series was over. The buzzer sounded, and the Warriors had taken a 3-0 chokehold over LeBron James and the Cavs. The LeBron James Ansh and I had grown up bonding over was about to become 3-5 in the NBA Finals.

---

29 "Mini-Movie: NBA Finals 2017 Game 3 | Warriors Win Thriller in Cleveland." Video file. YouTube. Posted by NBA, June 8, 2017. Accessed May 30, 2019. https://www.youtube.com/watch?v=xO21McAgIP0.

But Durant almost didn't get the chance to spoil our night. Mere days before the start of the 2014 NBA season, during his tenure in Oklahoma City, KD suffered a Jones fracture – a broken bone in his fifth metatarsal, right below his small toe – in his right foot.[30] According to Dr. David Geier, an orthopedic surgeon specializing in sports medicine, Jones fractures can take weeks to emerge. In fact, according to Dr. Geier, "It is actually fairly common in basketball, football and soccer players with repetitive stress on the area without enough time to heal. In theory, if an athlete develops a stress fracture of this area and continues to play, the repetitive impact could cause a nonunion of the stress fracture. Typically, though, the pain limits an athlete's ability to play through it. Orthopedic surgeons have gradually shifted to proceeding with surgery early with these fractures in athletes."[31] At the time of Durant's injury, Thunder general manager Sam Presti declared, "a Jones fracture is the most common surgical procedure performed on NBA players as of late. It has happened enough so that there is enough of a body of work to look at an average recovery time. He could

30 Young, Royce. "Kevin Durant Fractures Foot." ESPN. Last modified October 13, 2014. Accessed May 30, 2019. http://www.espn.com/nba/story/_/id/11688088/kevin-durant-oklahoma-city-thunder-fractured-foot.

31 Sherman, J. A. "Kevin Durant's foot injury and recovery: orthopaedic surgeon Dr. David Geier offers dispassionate analysis." Welcome to Loud City. Last modified October 13, 2014. Accessed May 30, 2019. https://www.welcometoloudcity.com/2014/10/13/6968383/kevin-durant-thunder-foot-jones-fracture-doctor-david-geier.

be playing on it today, but he'd be doing further damage to it, and eventually, we'd have more [of] an issue."[32] Coming off an MVP-winning season in which he averaged 32 points per game and legendarily declared that his mother was the real MVP, Durant's diagnosis had fans around the world unsure of whether one of the most prolific scorers in the history of the game would ever come back as the same player.

As a cloud of uncertainty surrounded Durant and his future with the Oklahoma City Thunder, GM Sam Presti was confident Durant would return to basketball as the incredible player he had grown to become over the course of his six seasons playing for the Thunder. Presti declared, "You have to be able to deal with uncertainty and ambiguity. If [you] can only operate [when] the wind is blowing out for you, I don't think that's the mark of an elite team or an elite organization. And I think Kevin is at his best when he has to experience something different. I think he'll find something good from this."[33]

That month, Durant had a screw inserted into his foot with the aim of speeding up the rate at which the stress fracture healed. This bone tends to heal slowly because it does

---

32 Ibid

33 ESPN.com News Services. "Kevin Durant Fractures Foot." ABC News. Last modified October 12, 2014. Accessed May 30, 2019. https://abcnews.go.com/Sports/kevin-durant-fractures-foot/story?id=26138491.

not naturally receive a large amount of blood supply.[34] As Durant took seven weeks off from basketball and missed the start of the season, the Thunder won only five games. After Durant came back and helped the Thunder win games with his scoring ability very much intact, he suffered a setback in February 2015 as he experienced extreme soreness in his surgically repaired foot. According to GM Sam Presti, upon consultation with Dr. Martin O'Malley, it was discovered that the screw that had previously been implanted into Durant's foot was rubbing up against another bone. Durant and his team opted to have Dr. O'Malley replace the screw that was giving Durant trouble with a headless fixture that was inserted deeper into his foot and did not rub against his cuboid bone and cause irritation.[35] According to Dr. O'Malley, "Pictures of Kevin's feet look like hockey sticks."[36] The curved, narrow shape of KD's feet made his recovery from this stress fracture particularly difficult. As Durant worked back from this second surgery on his foot, he suffered a

---

34 Sherman, J. A. "Kevin Durant's foot injury and recovery: orthopaedic surgeon Dr.David Geier offers dispassionate analysis." Welcome to Loud City. Last modified October 13, 2014. Accessed May 30, 2019. https://www.welcometoloudcity.com/2014/10/13/6968383/kevin-durant-thunder-foot-jones-fracture-doctor-david-geier.

35 Mayberry, Darnell. "Kevin Durant undergoes second surgery on right foot, will be reevaluated in one week." The Oklahoman. Last modified February 23, 2015. Accessed May 30, 2019. https://oklahoman.com/article/5395690/kevin-durant-undergoes-second-surgery-on-right-foot-will-be-reevaluated-in-one-week.

36 ESPN. "Why Kevin Durant sees world differently now." Hospital for Special Surgery. Last modified June 1, 2017. Accessed May 30, 2019. https://www.hss.edu/newsroom_espn-kevin-durant-nba-playoffs.asp.

second fracture in his foot a mere month after having surgery. And again, it was a stress fracture below the fifth metatarsal in his right foot. Another Jones fracture.[37]

This time around, Dr. O'Malley opted to perform a bone graft surgery on Durant's problematic foot. Although Jones fractures are a fairly common injury among basketball players and the guidelines regarding their treatment have become well-established, Durant's case was unique due to the shape of his foot and the recurrence of the injury. Dr. O'Malley recalls, "These were desperate times. I told Kevin, 'I've never had an NBA player lose his career over a Jones fracture.' But I couldn't cut and reshape Kevin's foot. It was scary. We were all freaking out a bit."[38] On March 31, 2015, Dr. O'Malley performed a bone graft surgery on KD's foot at the Hospital for Special Surgery in New York by utilizing bone from Durant's pelvis and then covering this graft with another synthetic graft composed of bone proteins, which served as a bony protective layer on Durant's foot. After this procedure was performed on Durant, he was unable to put weight on his foot for six weeks, ending his season.[39] KD recalls, "It was tough, it was tough. But it's all part of the journey I'm

---

37 Ibid
38 MacMullan, Jackie. "Why Kevin Durant sees world differently now." ESPN. Last modified June 1, 2017. Accessed May 30, 2019. http://www.espn.com/nba/story/_/page/presents-19505704/nba-playoffs-why-kevin-durant-sees-world-differently-now
39 Ibid

on, man. I'm just going to continue to stay positive and keep working hard, and everything will work out."[40]

Durant's self-confidence was a product of the trials and tribulations of his entire season as he had continuously dealt with foot issues. As Durant was looking forward to his rehabilitation process, he said, "Looking back on it now, there's a lot of stuff I would've changed, but it was necessary to go through what I had to go through, mentally, and I'm in a great space right now. Maybe because I'm closer and closer to playing again, but I'm in a great space."[41] For Durant, the focus had flipped from resting sufficiently to going all out in the gym. Durant was excited for the grueling work that was about to come, stating, "It is what it is, man. I'm just trying to continue focusing on getting better and rehabbing and killing that part of this journey and hopefully getting ready for next season. I think I gotta lose some weight, to be honest. But I've been putting in a lot of work in the weight room. I haven't moved at all for 12 or 13 weeks, so last week was really the first time I've got on the court and dropped some sweat."[42]

---

40 Young, Royce. "Kevin Durant expects to be fully cleared by August." ESPN. Last modified July 4, 2015. Accessed May 30, 2019. http://www. espn.com/nba/story/_/id/13199049/kevin-durant-oklahoma-city-thunder-tries-move-forward-season-ending-injury.

41 Young, Royce. "Kevin Durant expects to be fully cleared by August." ESPN. Last modified July 4, 2015. Accessed May 30, 2019. http://www. espn.com/nba/story/_/id/13199049/kevin-durant-oklahoma-city-thunder-tries-move-forward-season-ending-injury.

42 Ibid

In addition to physically putting himself in a position to bounce back strongly from his foot woes, Durant prided himself on establishing a mindset that was entirely centered around his rehabilitation process rather than other aspects of his career, such as the impending free agency decision he would have to make. Durant claimed, "No, I haven't thought about [free agency]. I hear it all the time, but I really am just focusing on rehab. I can't get there unless I take care of today. My main thing is just getting rid of distractions and focusing on what I have to do. I just can't wait to play the game I love again."[43]

After Durant had given himself ample time to rest and heal following his bone graft surgery, he was finally allowed back on the basketball court. Durant eased into his on-court rehab by shooting only jump shots and not sprinting or making cuts on the court. As he worked his jump shot back into shape, he was closely monitored by his medical team. According to Durant at the time, "We're doing x-rays every two weeks, and it's looking good. So I'm excited to get back. There's no pain and [I'm] looking forward to getting back."[44] Durant continued working on conditioning, using an anti-gravity treadmill that allowed him to work on his endurance and

---

43 Ibid
44 Ibid

cardiovascular health while drastically reducing the pressure on his surgically repaired foot.[45]

As KD worked himself back into game shape, he was cleared to play at the beginning of the 2015 NBA season. Durant refused to let his injury hold him back, recalling, "First two games I did, but I just realized if I'm out there playing, everything is all right. I'm still going to be aggressive like that going to the rim. I can live with whatever happens after that. I'm one of those guys that's going to play how I play if I'm out on the court. If I try to hold back and worry about what may happen, that's when I don't bring the edge I usually play with. Whatever happens, happens."[46]

As Durant played like his old self, icing games and proving himself worthy of the "Slim Reaper" nickname he had earned in years past, it was clear that the right foot that had given him so much trouble in the 2014-15 season had finally settled down with the help of his medical team. As Durant made a highly criticized free agency move to the already stacked Golden State Warriors prior to the 2016-2017 NBA season, it was clear that the one-time MVP was eager to add "NBA champion" to his résumé.

---

45   Gitlin, Marty. "Videos show Thunder star Kevin Durant accelerating rehab." CBS Sports. Last modified June 26, 2015. Accessed May 30, 2019. https://www.cbssports.com/nba/news/videos-show-thunder-star-kevin-durant-accelerating-rehab/.

46   ———. "Kevin Durant: Foot not a concern." ESPN. Last modified December 10, 2014. Accessed May 30, 2019. http://www.espn.com.au/nba/story/_/id/12010575/kevin-durant-oklahoma-city-thunder-not-worried-surgically-repaired-right-foot.

Durant's game-winning jumper over LeBron James in Game Three of the 2017 Finals marked a turning point in Durant's already storied, hall-of-fame-worthy career. As the Warriors would go on to win that series four games to one, Durant would go on to secure his first-ever career NBA title and NBA Finals MVP award. In the following season, the Warriors would go on to sweep a profoundly undermanned Cavaliers team that LeBron James dragged kicking and screaming to the finals, with Durant once again securing Finals MVP honors. Durant's chronic foot issues nearly derailed his illustrious career in its prime. Without the constant dedication of his medical team and the nuanced operations they performed on him, Durant would likely not have taken over the NBA in the way he has.

Reminiscing on his iconic, essentially championship-clinching 3 over LeBron in 2017, Durant said "That was the best moment I ever had. I made the game-winning shot in the Finals against my f-----g idol. Somebody that I really, really, really followed since I was a ninth-grade high-schooler. I felt like he was passing the torch to me"[47]

---

47 Bieler, Des. "Kevin Durant: Finals game-winner felt like LeBron James 'passing the torch' to him." The Washington Post. Last modified November 16, 2017. Accessed May 30, 2019. https://www.washingtonpost.com/news/early-lead/wp/2017/11/16/kevin-durant-finals-game-winner-felt-like-lebron-james-passing-the-torch-to-him/?utm_term=.a91a67e9171b.

CHAPTER 3

RUSSELL WESTBROOK: WHY NOT?

———

Surprisingly, Russell Westbrook was wearing a plain white shirt on stage – one not covered with polka dots or with a neon vest draped over it. It was an unusually normal look for the all-star point guard who prided himself on being anything but normal. As he started off his MVP speech by thanking God, the Oklahoma City Thunder, the media, the fans, and his agency, Westbrook was still bewilderingly normal. But as he thanked his parents, his voice quivered, and he took off his turquoise glasses to wipe his eyes. As he looked out toward the crowd and told them that his brother has texted him at the halftime of every game he has played in since he entered the NBA, tears started to trickle down his face. As he thanked his wife, struggling to find the words to express his gratitude for the sacrifices she had made for him over the years, ending with a charismatic "I love you, sugar" only he could have pulled off on a stage that grand, it was clear that the Russell Westbrook everyone had fallen in love with was on that stage, and that his journey to the MVP award was anything but normal.[48]

Three years before he had been proclaimed NBA MVP, in a game against the Houston Rockets, as Westbrook brought it up the left sideline, the whistle sounded as then-Thunder head coach Scott Brooks called a timeout. Almost immediately as the whistle sounded, the tenacious Rockets guard Patrick Beverley reached in to snatch the ball from Westbrook. Beverley collided with Westbrook's knee, and the two fell to the hardwood. As he sprung back up, Westbrook hopped over to the scorers' table on one leg and slapped the table violently, visibly enraged as he glared menacingly over at the Rockets' bench. The crowd was stunned, holding its collective breath. As he hobbled off the court and into the locker room, everyone seemed to understand the gravity of what had taken place before them.[49] The Thunder would go on to be eliminated in

48 "Russell Westbrook Full KIA MVP Presentation & Speech | NBA Awards 2017." Video file. YouTube. Posted by NBA, June 26, 2017. Accessed May 31, 2019. https://www.youtube.com/watch?v=vEg-jp8vkT4.

49 Winfield, Kristian. "A history of Russell Westbrook's many knee surgeries." SB Nation. Last modified September 12, 2018. Accessed May 31, 2019. https://www.sbnation.com/2018/9/12/17851948/russell-westbrook-knee-injury-surgery-history-thunder.

the next round of the playoffs by the Memphis Grizzlies that year without the motor of their team on the court to lead them.

MRIs showed that Westbrook had suffered a lateral meniscus tear in his right knee, which would likely keep him away from basketball for months. This was one of the same injuries that MVP point guard Derrick Rose had suffered, and while Rose eventually returned to the basketball court after surgery, he returned without the explosive athleticism known to catalyze his elite level of play. The question for Westbrook was not if he would return, but if he would return as the same guard known for viciously attacking the rim and playing at full speed at every possession of every game.[50]

After a team of surgeons repaired his meniscus, Westbrook was on crutches for around a month. He took to the video-sharing app Vine to play the air guitar on a crutch as he sang along to Taylor Swift's "Stay Stay Stay," in the light-hearted, fun-loving way that contrasted wildly with the ferocious assassin he was the moment he stepped foot on a basketball court.[51] But this jubilant recovery did not last

50 Conway, Tyler. "Timeline of Russell Westbrook's Journey from Knee Injury to NBA Return." Bleacher Report. Last modified November 3, 2013. Accessed May 31, 2019. https://bleacherreport.com/articles/1816655-timeline-of-russell-westbrooks-journey-from-knee-injury-to-nba-return.

51 Conway, Tyler. "Timeline of Russell Westbrook's Journey from Knee Injury to NBA Return." Bleacher Report. Last modified November 3, 2013. Accessed May 31, 2019. https://bleacherreport.com/articles/1816655-timeline-of-russell-westbrooks-journey-from-knee-injury-to-nba-return.

long, as on October 1, 2013, Westbrook had another surgery on his meniscus to repair a loose stitch that was causing his knee to remain swollen and uncomfortable.[52] Estimates at the time anticipated that Westbrook would miss at least the first month of the NBA season. Westbrook declared, "I want to play in every game as long as I'm able to and able to walk."[53] After working closely with the Thunder's trainers, Westbrook's rehabilitation timeline accelerated. The fears of Westbrook losing his athleticism seemed to dissipate as he put work in alongside the training staff to strengthen the ligaments in his right knee. His teammates swore he was "as explosive as ever." With the help of his doctors and training staff, Westbrook returned to the court on November 3, 2013, missing just two games instead of a full month.[54]

The incredible thing about Russell Westbrook is that he did not just return to his old form from a meniscus tear, but he came back even better. Two seasons after returning from an

---

52 Winfield, Kristian. "A history of Russell Westbrook's many knee surgeries." SB Nation. Last modified September 12, 2018. Accessed May 31, 2019. https://www.sbnation.com/2018/9/12/17851948/russell-westbrook-knee-injury-surgery-history-thunder.

53 "Westbrook speaks on injury, expected on crutches 4-5 weeks." NBA.com. Last modified May 9, 2013. Accessed May 31, 2019. https://www.nba.com/2013/news/05/09/westbrook-discusses-injury/.

54 Wojnarowski, Adrian. "Russell Westbrook returning to Thunder lineup against Suns." Yahoo! Sports. Last modified November 3, 2013. Accessed May 31,2019. https://ca.sports.yahoo.com/news/nba--russell-westbrook-could-return-to-thunder-lineup-within-two-weeks-003220954.html.

injury that many assumed would sap his legendary athleticism, Westbrook put up a few triple-doubles (notching at least 10 for three of the five main statistical categories: points, rebounds, assists, steals, and blocks), in his MVP-winning campaign: 42 triple-doubles, to be exact, the most in a single season in NBA history and more than MVP favorite and former teammate James Harden has in his entire career. Westbrook had become the first player to average a triple-double since all-time great Oscar Robertson accomplished the feat in 1962.[55] The record-breaking triple-double came when the Thunder needed it most, scratching and clawing for playoff positioning in the elite Western Conference with only three games left in the regular season. Down two points against the Nuggets in Denver with only 2.9 seconds remaining on the clock, the Thunder desperately needed a bucket. As the Thunder set up their inbound play and Westbrook darted in a circle around the perimeter, he could not create enough space to catch a pass. As Kyle Singler desperately looked for a person to throw it into, with time running out, he settled for a pass to the center Steven Adams, who was standing well beyond the three-point line. Almost instinctively, Adams turned around and found Westbrook, who was a good 10 feet behind the three-point line. Westbrook caught the pass with a hand in his face and a little under 2 seconds left on

---

55 "All-Time Leaders: Career Triple-Doubles." NBA.com. Last modified December 28, 2016. Accessed May 31, 2019. https://stats.nba.com/articles/all-time-leaders-career-triple-doubles/.

the clock, and without hesitation, he rose up smoothly over the defender and fired a shot at the basket. Dagger. As the announcer nonchalantly said "he got it," unsurprised by what he had just witnessed, Westbrook sprinted into the backcourt and was mobbed by his teammates.[56] That 35-footer gave him 50 points on the night to go along with 16 rebounds and 10 assists.[57] Westbrook's record-breaking 42nd triple-double knocked the Nuggets out of playoff contention while immortalizing his name in the record books.

As he mopped the sweat off of his forehead with his jersey for the postgame interview, watching the Nuggets exit the court, Westbrook thanked God, his teammates, his fans, and his family before adding in, "my motto is 'Why Not?'" in a way that was quintessentially Russ.[58] One thing became clear: Russell Westbrook's journey from a potentially career-derailing injury to a transcendent, once-in-a-generation, hall-of-fame-worthy run was anything but ordinary, and it would have been impossible without the proper medical team in

56 "Russell Westbrook NBA RECORD 42ND TRIPLE DOUBLE Full Game Highlights | April 9, 2017." Video file. YouTube. Posted by NBA, April 9, 2017. Accessed May 31, 2019. https://www.youtube.com/watch?v=sLwLoicdKsI.

57 "Russell Westbrook." ESPN. Last modified 2019. Accessed May 31, 2019. http://www.espn.com/nba/player/gamelog/_/id/3468/year/2017/russell-westbrook.

58 "Postgame Russell Westbrook Interview 42nd Triple Double! | April 9, 2017." Video file. YouTube. Posted by NBA Highlights, April 9, 2017. Accessed May 31, 2019. https://www.youtube.com/watch?v=56yjR8mTT6M.

place working tirelessly to get Westbrook's knee back to the elite level of functioning he was used to enjoying. And incredibly, the next season, Westbrook went out and averaged a triple-double again. Because why not?

CHAPTER 4

PAUL GEORGE: UNFINISHED BUSINESS

—

As Russell Westbrook got on the stage at his massive house party, telling the crowd to give a familiar face an "Oklahoma City welcome," the crowd produced a deafening roar. As Paul George picked up a mic and yelled "OKLAHOMA," the crowd got even louder. "If y'all didn't quite get it, let me say it again: I'm here to stay. I'm here to stay," George declared confidently. He further explained, "I think what we – me and this dude right here can accomplish," pointing to his MVP teammate on stage, "we can bring it home." As the crowd erupted into a frenzy, George further expressed his gratitude to Oklahoma City for showing love to him and his family. Finally, George affirmed, "I'm happy to give this a real shot."[59] It had been a tumultuous year for Paul George (affectionately called PG-13 by his fans) as his relationship with the Indiana Pacers deteriorated and he was incessantly linked to his hometown Los Angeles Lakers. After an unexpected trade sent George to the Thunder, it seemed that a move to the Lakers as George became a free agent after the 2017-18 season was all but inevitable. But after a playoff run with Russell Westbrook and several months playing with the most raucous crowd in the league supporting him, it became clear that George's offseason decision was exactly that – a decision. Not some prophecy set in stone. And as he later announced that night by posting a picture on Instagram, smoking cigars with his partner in crime Russell Westbrook, they had unfinished business.

All the uncertainty surrounding Paul George before he signed a monster four-year, $137 million deal with the Thunder paled in comparison to the uncertainty he faced in the months following August 2, 2014.[60] During these months, George was unsure if he would ever return to the basketball court. During a Team USA scrimmage at UNLV, George was chasing James Harden down for a block. George took off, attempting

---

59 "Russell Westbrook House Party Where Paul George Return | Behind-
    The-Scenes."Video file. YouTube. Posted July 7, 2018. Accessed May
    31, 2019. https://www.youtube.com/watch?v=-S2O5FR0Wk8.
60 "Paul George." Spotrac. Last modified 2019. Accessed May 31,
    2019. https://www.spotrac.com/nba/oklahoma-city-thunder/
    paul-george-6892/.

to glass the layup attempt. However, George landed with his leg against the basket stanchion. In an instant, his leg snapped, and he lay on the court motionless, with his hands on his head, watching the medical staff swarm around him.[61]

As soon he felt the air touch his wound, he felt a shockwave go through his body. Each moment became excruciatingly slow. "I could hear every individual in the arena talking," George would later recall. George remembered thinking, "Why can't I stand right now?" He later remembered the feeling of horror he felt when he saw his bone, shakily saying "The second I saw my bone I lost it. I just laid flat." As George's dad, Paul Sr., came down from the stands and held his hand, the intense pain would not stop radiating through his body. As he was transferred to an ambulance, his mom, Paulette, kept rubbing his hands, promising him, "you're going to be ok," while thinking to herself, "I hope his career isn't over."[62]

As George was brought to Sunrise Hospital, where he would eventually spend three agonizingly long days, Team USA Head Coach Mike Krzyzewski had decided to end the scrimmage. George, who just days ago had said that being a part

---

61 NBA Highlights. "Paul George breaks his leg... - Team USA - Blue vs White 2014."YouTube. Last modified August 1, 2014. Accessed May 31, 2019. https://www.youtube.com/watch?v=Fi2RoIlCXlA.

62 B/R Studios. "Paul George's Road Back: Reliving the Nightmare Ep. 1." Bleacher Report. Accessed May 31, 2019. https://bleacherreport.com/articles/2344193-paul-georges-road-back-reliving-the-nightmare-ep-1.

of Team USA was "bigger than just basketball" and that he was thrilled to have been selected to represent the nation, was now in danger of never playing the sport again.[63]

Upon reaching the hospital, George was informed by the medical staff that he had broken his tibia and fibula in a compound fracture and that he would have a metal rod implanted into his shin with three screws in order to support his leg. Prior to his freak injury, George said "I felt I was immortal." Countless times, he remembered, he had fallen down and had "walked up clean from it. I did feel that nothing bad could happen to me on the court."[64] Dr. Riley Williams, a Team USA physician, successfully performed the surgery on George with Dr. David Silverberg and Dr. Joseph Yu.[65] George credits the medical staff for helping him wrap his head around his injury and subsequent return from it, recalling, "not too long after surgery and speaking to the doctors, I knew I'd be back to this point. The only question in my

---

63   Amick, Sam. "Paul George recovering from surgery for fracture." USA Today. Last modified August 2, 2014. Accessed May 31, 2019. https://www.usatoday.com/story/sports/nba/pacers/2014/08/02/paul-george-surgery-compound-fracture-tibia-fibula-team-usa/13505781/.

64   B/R Studios. "Paul George's Road Back: Reliving the Nightmare Ep. 1." Bleacher Report. Accessed May 31, 2019. https://bleacherreport.com/articles/2344193-paul-georges-road-back-reliving-the-nightmare-ep-1.

65   Gatto, Tom. "Paul George suffers broken leg during Team USA scrimmage." SportingNews. Last modified August 1, 2014. Accessed May 31, 2019. https://www.sportingnews.com/us/other-sports/news/paul-george-gruesome-injury-team-usa-fiba-world-cup-pacers/1b-mm64ta9bo8m1mm4lfq15ukun.

mind was when, not if. When."[66] Pacers coach Frank Vogel reiterated the value of the doctors in allowing George to be in the proper state of mind to make a recovery, remembering, "When the doctors told him the surgery was successful, that's all he needed to hear."[67] Now, sitting in a Las Vegas hospital room with a metal rod in his surgically reconstructed leg, George faced not only the physical hurdle of getting himself back in game shape, but the mental hurdle that accompanied the realization that he was by no means invincible.

Four days after he got back from the hospital, George placed a chair in the middle of the paint at the basketball court in his house, shooting baskets as he was sitting. Two or three weeks after his surgery, George realized the gravity of the difficulties that lay ahead. He remembers being stuck in the same room for 12 to 13 hours because he was too weak to move. The former MVP candidate recalls, "I would be out of breath to go from downstairs to upstairs." But as he lay in bed at home, the Pacers cornerstone looked to his father and without a glimmer of doubt in his eyes, declared, "when I come back,

66 Powell, Shaun. "For Pacers' leading man, comeback has been completed." NBA.com. Last modified February 8, 2016. Accessed May 31, 2019. https://www.nba.com/2016/news/features/shaun_powell/02/08/paul-george-all-the-way-back-to-all-star-level.

67 B/R Studios. "Paul George's Road Back: Reliving the Nightmare Ep. 1." Bleacher Report. Accessed May 31, 2019. https://bleacherreport.com/articles/2344193-paul-georges-road-back-reliving-the-nightmare-ep-1.

I'm going to come back a beast."[68] As the weeks progressed, he shot jumpers with a boot on before he was back to shooting regular jump shots. Then-teammate David West recalled that George "immediately pushed his focus on getting back, getting stronger, getting healthy." Dr. Riley Williams proudly remembers George's mental determination to come back as an even better player, recalling, "he didn't ask me 'is the bone going to heal,' he asked me 'when am I going to be able to play again.'"[69] As George rehabbed hard, putting in countless hours in the gym with trainers and physical therapists, he began to look like himself again. As he discussed his injury, George affectionately referred to his implanted rod and joked, "It's a part of me. Extra bone!" George had already dreamed of his return. "I'm going to make a big play, hopefully it's my first shot, and then I'm turning to the crowd to let them know I'm back."[70] Six months after undergoing surgery, Paul George was back in the practice facility, throwing down dunks.[71]

68 "Paul George The Road Back The Lost Season? Episode 3." Video file. YouTube. Posted by Ball_Motivation, March 20, 2015. Accessed May 31, 2019. https://www.youtube.com/watch?v=7d3NaNnThaw

69 Duffy, Thomas. "The doctor and the superstar." Nets Daily. Last modified April 6, 2015. Accessed May 31, 2019. https://www.netsdaily.com/2015/4/6/8322857/will-paul-george-kill-the-nets-playoff-chances.

70 "Paul George The Road Back The Lost Season? Episode 3." Video file. YouTube. Posted by Ball_Motivation, March 20, 2015. Accessed May 31, 2019.

71 Newport, Kyle. "Paul George Is Dunking in Practice 6 Months After Gruesome Leg Injury." Bleacher Report. Last modified January 15, 2015. Accessed May 31, 2019. https://bleacherreport.com/articles/2331388-paul-george-is-dunking-in-practice-6-months-after-gruesome-leg-injury.

On April 5, 2015, Paul George checked into the game with 5:34 left in the first quarter. As he stepped onto the floor of an organized game of basketball for the first time in eight months, the Indiana crowd burst into thunderous cheers and applause. George felt time slow down much as it had when he lay on the floor at UNLV with a bone poking out of his leg. Only this time, instead of pain, he felt bliss. As George caught the ball at the right wing, he pivoted to the basket and quickly shook his defender off on a screen before pulling up over two swarming Heat defenders. As George leaned and faded, his shot sank effortlessly off the back iron. Then he turned and nodded to the crowd just like he had drawn it up in his head for months. He let them know he was back.[72]

"I'm sure some people thought my career was over," George reminisced, having recently been voted into the 2016 NBA All-Star Game.[73] About 18 months after breaking his leg, George had lofted himself back into the elite rung of the NBA with an All-Star Game appearance as the cherry on top. After he endured a massively invasive surgery and grinded through months upon months of physical therapy with the Pacers medical staff, Paul George was not only playing professional

---

72 "Paul George's return after broken leg + first points! (04.05.2015)." Video file. YouTube. Posted by NBAHighlights2, April 5, 2015. https://www.youtube.com/watch?v=9uPND2JKKSI.

73 Powell, Shaun. "For Pacers' leading man, comeback has been completed." NBA.com. Last modified February 8, 2016. Accessed May 31, 2019. https://www.nba.com/2016/news/features/shaun_powell/02/08/paul-george-all-the-way-back-to-all-star-level.

basketball, but the best basketball of his life. As George made the move to Oklahoma City while garnering all-star honors in the 2017 and 2018 seasons, it became apparent that his highly improbable comeback had indeed become a reality with the coordinated help of his physicians and physical therapists. Having achieved a remarkable recovery, George is now setting his sights on a quest for a championship. PG-13 is back, and he has some unfinished business.

CHAPTER 5

KOBE BRYANT: MAMBA MODE

———

I squeezed into my grandparents' queen bed as my grandma and grandpa slowly edged to the sides of the bed to make space for me in the middle. This was how we always watched TV together when they came over, and even though I was now 18, I instinctively jumped into the position I was used to my whole life. As my grandma changed the channel from Zee TV to TNT, begrudgingly accepting that she would have to catch up on her Hindi serials later, I anxiously prepared myself, unsure of what I would feel or how I was supposed to feel. As the Lakers vs. Jazz matchup was set to start, I began to realize that this was going to be the last time I would be able to watch Kobe Bryant play. For as long as I can remember, my grandpa and I would watch Kobe hit impossible shot after impossible shot. For as long as I can remember, I would swear he was the greatest scorer I had ever seen, to which my grandpa would retort that I didn't remember watching Michael Jordan play. As the opening tipoff began, I turned to my grandpa and said, "I just hope he gets 20. Under that would be embarrassing for Kobe." My grandpa turned his head to me, and as reassuringly as he always was, replied "Trust me, he'll get his 20. I'll bet Kobe finishes with at least 30. The great ones always find a way to get it done." As the first quarter came to a close, it was becoming clear that we were witnessing something special. Bryant had 15 points — as many as Jordan had in his entire last game.[74]

By the end of the first half, Bryant had scored 22 points. The Lakers fans booed every time anyone other than the Black Mamba touched the ball. 37 points by the end of the third.[75] At this point, I had stopped worrying about whether Bryant would embarrass himself, as the only people getting embarrassed were the Jazz defenders who needed a win for playoff positioning and were getting torched by the 37-year-old Bryant on his last legs. I looked over at my grandpa, asking him if he had dozed off during the break between quarters. He stared right back at me and before I could say a word,

74 "Utah Jazz at Los Angeles Lakers Play-By-Play, April 13, 2016." Basketball Reference. Accessed May 31, 2019. https://www.basketball-reference.com/boxscores/pbp/201604130LAL.html.

75 Ibid

chuckled, "No way I'm falling asleep during this game, you don't need to check on me."

At the start of the fourth quarter, the Lakers found themselves down by nine to a Jazz team that looked hungry to spoil Kobe's last rodeo. With a little over 9 minutes remaining, he stepped into a transition three-pointer. As the low-arcing shot splashed into the net, Bryant had himself a 40-point night. The 135th of his career. As the fourth quarter wound down, with a little over two minutes remaining, the Lakers found themselves in the same hole they had been in all game, down by 10 points. Kobe had 47 points. He had done more than was expected of him in his last game, showing the world how he had earned his legacy as being one of the most prolific scorers to ever lace up a pair of low-top sneakers. But scoring 47 points in his last hurrah was not enough for one of the fiercest competitors in the history of sports. If there was one thing Kobe wanted throughout his career, it was to win. And he was hellbent on winning his last game in the purple and gold.[76]

Bryant drove hard to the rim, getting bumped by Gordon Hayward as he missed a tough layup. He went to the line and knocked down two free throws. 49 points for Bryant.

76 "Kobe Bryant final game fourth quarter only shots." Video file. You-Tube. Posted by Marc S, April 17, 2016. Accessed May 31, 2019. https://www.youtube.com/watch?v=KjvUxW6NoRA.

8-point game. The following possession, he drove to the rim again, absorbing contact under the basket as he flipped up a shot that kissed off the top of the backboard and delicately fell through the basket. 51. 6-point game. The crowd erupted as the TV announcer happily declared "A 50-point game in his farewell!"[77] My grandparents and I were at the edge of our seats now. My grandma doesn't like basketball, but she knew she was witnessing something special as she sat with her eyes glued to the screen.

"Kobe! Kobe! Kobe!" chanted the crowd, as Bryant dribbled the ball up the court. As two Jazz defenders swarmed him as he reached the free-throw line, Kobe quickly dribbled the ball between them and stopped on a dime at the free-throw line, rising up for a graceful jump shot that fell easily through the basket. 53. 4-point game. The camera panned to die-hard Lakers fan Jack Nicholson, who could do nothing but shake his head and say, "wow."

As the Jazz failed to score on offense again, the entire Staples Center crowd erupted as the ball was bounced to Kobe. He brought it up the floor, and after a hesitation dribble, he stepped to the side and launched a fadeaway three-pointer over a taller defender. The shot sank effortlessly like hundreds of Kobe Bryant fadeaways of years past. 56. 1-point

---

77 Ibid

game. As the Jazz called a timeout and Kobe ran to the Lakers huddle, Jay-Z looked around in shock from his courtside seat. Bryant's wife and kids celebrated as Kobe sat on the bench, looking absolutely gassed, reaching deep down for the willpower to finish this game.[78]

The Jazz missed a three-point attempt, and my grandpa and I looked at each other and at the same time, blurted out, "Kobe is going to win this." As the Lakers gained possession, the ball went straight to Kobe. As he maneuvered around the top of the three-point line and drove to the right laterally, two Jazz defenders desperately scrambled towards him as he pulled up just inside the three-point line. As Kobe faded back and kicked his leg out in signature Black Mamba fashion, my grandparents and I sat up. After what felt like an eternity, the shot splashed through the net and the buzzing murmurs of the crowd were converted into raucous cheers. 58. The Lakers finally had a lead.[79]

As Utah called a timeout, Kobe's Bryant's teammates mobbed him as his former teammate Shaquille O'Neal smiled jubilantly in the crowd. As the timeout came to an end, the Jazz inbounded the ball and quickly attempted a layup, which rolled right off the rim. As the ball bounced around, it was

---

78 Ibid
79 Ibid

finally gathered by Jordan Clarkson, who instantly kicked the ball out to Kobe. As he tread into the front court, he was grabbed by Jazz defenders the moment he passed half court in a desperate intentional foul, stopping the clock and sending Kobe to the free throw line. As Bryant wiped the sweat off of his dripping forehead onto the inside of his jersey before rubbing his hands on the soles of his signature Nikes, the sea of Lakers fans produced a low rumbling cacophony. As Kobe put the first free throw in, the rumble grew louder. 59. As he rubbed his hands on the front of his jersey and stepped back up to the free-throw line, my grandparents and I sat anxiously awaiting the release of the next shot. Kobe raised the ball above his head and quickly snapped his wrist forward. The ball took a perfect rainbow arc, sinking through the hoop. The crowd became deafeningly loud. 60.

The Lakers ran back on defense as Gordon Hayward attacked the rim. As Hayward flipped up a layup, the shot bounced off the backboard and the rim and was gathered by Julius Randle. Randle flipped the ball to who else but Kobe Bryant. Kobe dribbled the ball once before launching the ball down the court to a wide-open Jordan Clarkson, who threw it down hard with two hands. As the Jazz called another timeout, the Lakers swarmed to Kobe and hugged him. Shaq came down to the court and embraced his longtime partner in crime. Bryant sat down with the look of a cold blooded assassin.

The Lakers were up by 5 with four seconds remaining. He had iced the game.[80]

After the final buzzer sounded and Bryant hugged his family, he made his way to the Lakers logo at midcourt, where he was handed a microphone. "Man!" yelled Kobe, as he gripped the microphone. The crowd went wild. "I can't believe how fast 20 years went by, man, it's just crazy. It's just absolutely crazy, and you know, to be standing here at center court with you guys, my teammates behind me, and appreciating all this, you know, the journey that we have been on, we've been through our ups and been through our downs, and I think the most important part is we all stayed together throughout. I grew up a die-hard, I mean a die-hard Laker fan, die-hard. I mean, I knew everything about every player that has ever played here. So to be drafted and then traded to this organization and to spend 20 years here, you can't write something better than this. And I'm more proud, not about the championships, but about the down years. Because we didn't run. We didn't run. We played through all that stuff, and we got our championships, and we did it the right way. All I can do here is thank you guys, thank you guys for all the years of support, thank you guys for all the motivation, thank you for all the inspiration. The thing that had me cracking

---

80 "Kobe Bryant final game fourth quarter only shots." Video file. You-Tube. Posted by Marc S, April 17, 2016. Accessed May 31, 2019. https://www.youtube.com/watch?v=KjvUxW6N0RA.

up all night long was that I go through 20 years of everybody screaming 'pass the ball,' and then the last night they're like don't pass it. This has been absolutely beautiful. I can't believe it's come to an end. You guys will always be in my heart. I sincerely, sincerely appreciate it. No words can describe how I feel about you guys. Thank you, thank you from the bottom of my heart. I love you guys, I love you guys. My family, to my family, my wife Vanessa, my daughters Natalia and Gianna. Thank you, guys, for all your sacrifices. For all the time I spend in the gym and training, Vanessa you holding down the family the way that you have, there is no way I can thank you enough for that. From the bottom of my heart, thank you. What can I say, Mamba out."[81] As Kobe said those iconic last words, he placed the microphone on the ground. Bryant had just experienced a farewell experience fitting for a legend like him. Thankfully, he got to leave the game on his own terms. But he almost didn't get this opportunity. Years before he stepped away from basketball after his final 60-point outburst, Bryant's career was almost cut short by a devastating Achilles injury.

On April 12, 2013, as a Lakers team desperate for a playoff berth faced off against the Golden State Warriors, Kobe Bryant was locked in. The Lakers had been heavily relying on

---

81 "Kobe Bryant's Final Game Farewell Speech." Video file. YouTube. Posted by Mr. Mafeeny Chuggart, April 13, 2016. Accessed May 31, 2019. https://www.youtube.com/watch?v=pOHQWCqNV9E.

Kobe the past few games, needing every point they could muster to try to catapult themselves into the playoff picture in a notoriously tough Western Conference. With a little over three minutes remaining in the game, Bryant called for the ball with his back to the basket at the top of the three-point line. He had played the entirety of the game thus far. Bryant caught the pass and slowly pivoted to the rim before quickly cutting towards the basket. After a singular dribble, he slid to the floor, immediately gripping the back of his lower left leg. The referees blew their whistles, calling a blocking foul on Warriors forward Harrison Barnes. Bryant sat on the sleek hardwood floor of the Staples Center a little while longer, the gravity of the situation becoming quickly apparent to him as his foot refused to rotate. Trying his best to hide a grimace, he was helped up by his teammates. As he leaned on long-time teammate and fellow NBA champion Pau Gasol, Bryant could barely move, slowly making his way over to the Lakers' bench. The Lakers' trainer looked at Bryant's leg, and then, very slowly, Bryant gingerly waddled over to the free-throw line, unable to rotate his left foot at all.[82]

If Bryant went immediately to the locker room, the Lakers would be forced to forfeit the free throws he was awarded. And at this stage of the game, at this stage of the season,

82   "Kobe Bryant s torn achilles + shoots freethrows_medium." Video file. YouTube. Posted by Celse Dav, April 26, 2013. Accessed May 31, 2019. https://www.youtube.com/watch?v=g2afNT_7c90.

the Lakers needed every single point they could possibly score. A cold-blooded killer on the basketball court, Bryant did not even briefly consider the prospect of surrendering the free throws to begin receiving treatment for the excruciating pain that was shooting through the leg that had logged thousands of NBA minutes. Bryant coolly stepped up to the free throw line and knocked down two clutch free throws. Immediately after, the Lakers fouled the Warriors to stop play so the heroic Bryant could be helped off the court. The diagnosis seemed apparent just by looking at the difficulty in Bryant's movements: an Achilles tendon tear.

"When I first did it, right there, I was trying to feel if the tendon is there or if it's gone," recalled Bryant, whose immediate goal was to find a way to remain in the game. "I realized it wasn't there. I was literally trying to pull the tendon up, so hopefully I could walk and kind of hobble through the last two and a half minutes and try to play." After he knocked down what have now come to be regarded as legendary free throws, Kobe slowly inched his way to the locker room with a heavy heart. Soon after, though, Bryant turned this self-pity into fuel: "I was really tired, man. Just tired in the locker room, upset and dejected and thinking about this ... mountain, man, to overcome. I mean this is a long process. I wasn't sure I could do it. But then your kids walked in and you're like, I gotta to set an example.

'Daddy's going to be fine. I'm going to do it.' I'm going to work hard and go from there."[83]

The following day, Dr. Neal ElAttrache and Dr. Stephen Lombardo of the Kerlan-Jobe Institute performed a surgery on Bryant's left leg to repair his torn Achilles tendon, confirming the sports world's worst fear. Dr. ElAttrache compared the physical concept of the procedure to stitching two ends of a mop together. Bryant credited the surgeons for masterfully repairing his torn Achilles, claiming, "It was pretty innovative, the procedure that we did, in terms of how we attached the tendon and where it was torn. It was a really complicated procedure that they normally do when taking tendons from the big toe and bringing them in, but we really simplified the procedure and took a risk with it. A calculated risk. And it's been very successful for us."[84]

Bryant faced a lengthy rehabilitation process ahead of him following the procedure. According to Dr. ElAttrache, "You want to get them weight-bearing as soon as possible, to some

83 Murphy, David. "Timeline of Kobe Bryant's Return from Devastating Achilles Injury." Bleacher Report. Last modified December 6, 2013. Accessed May 31, 2019. https://bleacherreport.com/articles/1856278-timeline-of-kobe-bryants-return-from-devastating-achilles-injury.

84 Ding, Kevin. "Kobe Bryant's Maniacal Ambition a Challenge to His Aging Body." Bleacher Report. Last modified October 4, 2013. Accessed May 31, 2019. https://bleacherreport.com/articles/1798900-kobe-bryants-maniacal-ambition-a-challenge-to-his-aging-body.

degree, but it's got to be in a protected way, he said. Early on, the tendon is malleable and stretchable, so you want to get them using the muscle and getting on their leg and weight bearing for all the other reasons, even the remote reasons like the hip and the back and all the muscles in the lower leg. All that without stretching the tendon." Although the recovery time suggested by the physicians was between 6 and 9 months, Achilles injuries have also been known to take up to an entire year to recover from.[85]

With a long road of recovery ahead of him at the tail end of his career, Bryant took to Facebook to share his thoughts, declaring:

"This is such BS! All the training and sacrifice just flew out the window with one step that I've done millions of times! The frustration is unbearable. The anger is rage. Why the hell did this happen ?!? Makes no damn sense. Now I'm supposed to come back from this and be the same player Or better at 35?!? How in the world am I supposed to do that??

I have NO CLUE. Do I have the consistent will to overcome this thing? Maybe I should break out the rocking chair and reminisce on the career that was. Maybe this is how my

---

85   Farmer, Sam. "Exclusive: Doctor who performed Kobe Bryant's surgery is optimistic." Los Angeles Times. Last modified April 14, 2013. Accessed May 31, 2019. https://www.latimes.com/sports/lakers/ la-xpm-2013-apr-14-la-sp-ln-kobe-bryant-achilles-surgery-20130414-story.html.

book ends. Maybe Father Time has defeated me...Then again maybe not! ... One day, the beginning of a new career journey will commence. Today is NOT that day.... That's 'mamba mentality' we don't quit, we don't cower, we don't run. We endure and conquer."[86]

Bryant's famous "Mamba Mentality" served as a major asset during the challenging recovery and rehab process that was looming. Immediately after undergoing surgery, Bryant had to wait for several weeks before he could work on strengthening his surgically repaired Achilles tendon. According to Bryant, "With the tendon, there's really only but so much you can do. There's a certain amount of time that they deem necessary for the tendon to heal where you don't overstretch it and now you never get that spring back. So you just have to be patient, let the tendon heal, and then when that moment comes when they say, 'OK, we can take off the regulator, so to speak, and now it's on you to train as hard as you can to get back to where you want to be,' that's going to be a good day.'"[87]

86 Bryant, Kobe. *Facebook* (blog). Entry posted April 13, 2013. Accessed May 31, 2019. https://www.facebook.com/kobe/posts/this-is-such-bs-all-the-training-and-sacrifice-just-flew-out-the-window-with-one/10151563315250419/.

87 Onslow, Justin. "Kobe Bryant Targets 2013 Season Opener for Return from Achilles Tear." Bleacher Report. Last modified June 3, 2013. Accessed May 31, 2019. https://bleacherreport.com/articles/1660861-kobe-bryant-targets-opening-night-of-next-season-to-return-from-achilles-tear.

For the first nine days after undergoing surgery, Bryant had to wear a cast around his freshly repaired Achilles tendon.

On April 22, Bryant was freed from the constraints of his cast, which was replaced by a walking boot that allowed for more mobility. Around the same time, Bryant was able to start basic physical therapy as there was no significant pain or swelling caused by the removal of the cast and the transition into a walking boot. By the end of the month, the stitches that remained in Kobe's foot were removed.[88]

Bryant's rehab process was progressing as planned. Up to this point, there were no major bumps along the road, and he desperately wanted to work on his conditioning and his basketball ability in an effort to be in peak shape for the beginning of the upcoming season. To regain basic mobility and become reacclimated to motions he once took for granted, Bryant began walking on an AlterG anti-gravity treadmill, which allowed him to begin gradually strengthening his legs and work on his conditioning while reducing the impact that walking had on his still-delicate foot and Achilles. The special treadmill contains a compartment that is pressurized, which serves as a counterforce to the runner's body weight

---

88   Kay, Alex. "Breaking Down the Steps of Kobe Bryant's Return from Achilles Tear." Bleacher Report. Last modified December 8, 2013. Accessed May 31, 2019. https://bleacherreport.com/articles/1780056-breaking-down-the-steps-of-kobe-bryants-return-from-achilles-tear.

and reduces the strain on their body. Kobe ran on the AlterG in "Medical Mamba" shoes that sponsor Nike custom-made to provide additional reinforcement to his healing tendon.[89]

By July, Bryant was back on the court, shooting free throws. He was grateful for his physical therapist and the surgeons who operated on him almost immediately after diagnosing him with a torn Achilles, announcing, "It's progressing faster than everybody expected. I should be able to be more active with conditioning in the middle of August, which is like four months after the surgery. It's crazy, but I've been very, very fortunate to be able to have [Lakers head physical therapist] Judy [Seto] travel with me absolutely everywhere, be with me all the time, and I was fortunate to be able to go in and have the procedure done the next day [after the injury]. I think all that's helped."[90] Bryant asserted that the innovative, unique nature of the surgery he underwent was also largely responsible for his accelerated recovery timetable. According to Bryant, "The thing about this injury is that the surgical procedure was different. And because of that, the recovery has been different. The timetable has been different. You

---

89 Murphy, David. "Timeline of Kobe Bryant's Return from Devastating Achilles Injury." Bleacher Report. Last modified December 6, 2013. Accessed May 31, 2019. https://bleacherreport.com/articles/1856278-timeline-of-kobe-bryants-return-from-devastating-achilles-injury.

90 Murphy, David. "Timeline of Kobe Bryant's Return from Devastating Achilles Injury." Bleacher Report. Last modified December 6, 2013. Accessed May 31, 2019. https://bleacherreport.com/articles/1856278-timeline-of-kobe-bryants-return-from-devastating-achilles-injury.

know, the normal timetable for recovering for an Achilles, we've shattered that. You know, three and a half months, I can already walk just fine, I'm lifting weights for the Achilles just fine, and that's different. This is kind of new territory for us all."[91]

By August, Bryant was now running on the AlterG treadmill he had started just walking on. As the months progressed, he began gradually increasing the pressure allowed on his foot by using the treadmill on more difficult settings. Bryant continued to scale up rehab exercises, claiming, "It feels good just to run and break a sweat by running."[92] Dr. Joshua S. Dines, an orthopedic surgeon and sports medicine specialist who worked with the Los Angeles Lakers during the Kobe Bryant era, recalls the pure passion Bryant had for putting in the work required to be great and to return from injury. According to Dr. Dines, "Kobe more than anybody else, when you start talking about the Lakers and the NBA, he's unbelievably talented, but even amongst other talented people — and you know, all of them are in the NBA, all of them are

91 Pincus, Eric. "Kobe Bryant says he 'shattered' Achilles recovery timetable." Los Angeles Times. Last modified August 5, 2013. Accessed May 31, 2019. https://www.latimes.com/sports/lakers/la-xpm-2013-aug-05-la-sp-ln-kobe-bryant-achilles-20130805-story.html.

92 Murphy, David. "Timeline of Kobe Bryant's Return from Devastating Achilles Injury." Bleacher Report. Last modified December 6, 2013. Accessed May 31, 2019. https://bleacherreport.com/articles/1856278-timeline-of-kobe-bryants-return-from-devastating-achilles-injury.

getting paid a lot of money, and they are all working hard —
he just worked harder than everybody else. You would think
it would almost just equalize when you get to the highest
levels. But it's Kobe Bryant. What I found most impressive
about Kobe is that despite having the most talent, he was
also the person who worked the hardest and he got there the
earliest and left the latest, which was really humbling and
impressive to see."

By mid-November, Kobe was taking part in light basketball drills with the Lakers for the first time since tearing his Achilles. According to teammate Pau Gasol, "He
looked good and did a few moves I didn't expect him to
do right away. I'm very happy for him and for us, and definitely looking forward to when he'll play in a game."[93] For-
tunately for Gasol and the rest of the Lakers, on November
18, Bryant was medically cleared to continue all basketball
activities. Kobe was excited to get back into the action, but
also wanted to make sure his career would be preserved
in the long run, stating "It's definitely something where
you're kind of champing at the bit a little bit, but we've
come so far. I want to make sure, we all do, when you
step out there you're ready to go the long haul, and it's
not something that continues on. ... You just have to get

---

93   Ibid

stronger, but I could adjust my game and play at a pretty high level right now."[94]

On November 25, Kobe Bryant signed a two-year contract extension with the Lakers. With the help of his medical and therapy team, Bryant greatly exceeded expectations with regards to his recovery and had the Lakers organization excited for the future. Then-Lakers general manager Mitch Kupchak announced, "This is a very happy day for Lakers fans and for the Lakers organization. We've said all along that our priority and hope was to have Kobe finish his career as a Laker, and this should ensure that that happens. To play 20 years in the NBA, and to do so with the same team, is unprecedented, and quite an accomplishment. Most importantly however, it assures us that one of the best players in the world will remain a Laker, bringing us excellent play and excitement for years to come."[95] Bryant was also thrilled to have his future with the team secured, citing a mutual loyalty between him and the franchise as a cornerstone to their relationship. According to Bryant, "The only number I saw was the one I agreed to. The Lakers are a stand-up organization, and they stepped up to the plate

---

94 Ibid

95   Murphy, David. "Timeline of Kobe Bryant's Return from Devastating Achilles Injury." Bleacher Report. Last modified December 6, 2013. Accessed May 31, 2019. https://bleacherreport.com/articles/1856278-timeline-of-kobe-bryants-return-from-devastating-achilles-injury.

and took care of it. Some of it obviously was from work previously done, and some of the things I've done for the organization, and some of it was a leap of faith of what they expect me to do when I return."[96]

Two things were certain: Kobe Bryant was ready to return, and the Lakers were more than ready to have him back. An eager Bryant was confident in the work he put in to bounce back from the injury many swore was career-ending. "My legs feel fresh, and I feel very confident about where I'm at. Control what you can control, right? I've done my part. I've had to play through a season where there was much more on the line than whether or not I can come back from an Achilles injury, right? So those experiences don't make this a very stressful situation. If anything, I enjoy it. If there is an element of doubt as far as my game goes and being old age or something like that, I don't think that holds any value. The fact that I was playing my best basketball before I got hurt, injury is a thing, right, so we have to see who's ready. I feel great. And I'm back."[97] And on December 8, 2013, Kobe was back against the Toronto Raptors, less than eight months after tearing

96 Ibid

97 "Kobe Bryant 'Control What You Can Control' Achilles Recovery Inspirational." Video file. YouTube. Posted by NBA Highlights Non-stop, May 26, 2015. Accessed May 31, 2019. https://www.youtube.com/watch?v=LxvrOE4-J8s.

his Achilles tendon and having many doubters write off his career as finished.[98]

20 seasons with one team. Slam Dunk Champion. 81 points in a single game. Two-time Olympic Gold Medalist. 12 All-Defensive Team selections. 17-time NBA All Star. Two-time NBA Finals MVP. Five-time NBA Champion.[99] 60 points in his last NBA game. Kobe Bean Bryant has had a priceless imprint on the game of basketball. A legend like Kobe deserved nothing less than an iconic final game where he was able to exit the court on his own terms to thunderous applause one last time. He would not have gotten the last dance he deserved if it were not for his team of physicians and therapists. Thanks to his medical team, the basketball world's last memory of Kobe Bryant as a basketball player is that of a lethal scorer capable of singlehandedly shredding another team, not that of a helpless 34-year-old who could barely walk off the court in an essentially meaningless game. Thanks to his medical team, I got to watch Mamba Mode one last time.

98 Murphy, David. "Timeline of Kobe Bryant's Return from Devastating Achilles Injury." Bleacher Report. Last modified December 6, 2013. Accessed May 31, 2019. https://bleacherreport.com/articles/1856278-timeline-of-kobe-bryants-return-from-devastating-achilles-injury.

99 "Career Highlights." Mamba Out. Accessed May 31, 2019. http://mambaout.com/achievements.html.

CHAPTER 6

SHAUN LIVINGSTON: WINNING THE CHAMPIONSHIP

———

As the highlights continued to roll, showing Shaun Livingston bury pull-up jumpers followed by turnaround fadeaways followed by more pull-up jumpers, my friends and I arose from the plush couch in my friend Ansh's basement. We desperately wanted LeBron James to find a way to take down the Golden State Warriors in the 2016 NBA Finals. This was the year the Warriors had gone 73-9 — the best regular season record in NBA history. This was the year Stephen Curry had become the first ever unanimous MVP in NBA history. And although James would eventually find a way to take this team down in seven games in one of the greatest sports comeback stories ever, after Game One, the chances of anything going the Cleveland Cavaliers' way seemed bleak. The story of the night was Shaun Livingston. Although he was a solid bench player for the Warriors, he likely could have been a starting point guard on many NBA teams. In Game One, Stephen Curry and Klay Thompson, affectionately referred to as "The Splash Brothers" by basketball fans for their three-point shooting prowess, combined for just 20 points. Draymond Green, the Warriors' best defender and an All-Star power forward, only had 16. Veteran guard Andre Iguodala, the NBA Finals MVP for the Warriors in the previous season, was only able to add 12 points. At first glance, there was no way the Warriors could have won this game. But behind Shaun Livingston's huge 20 points, most of which came when the Warriors needed them most, the Warriors were able to secure a 15-point win to start off the 2015 NBA Finals.[100]

Livingston certainly always had the potential to accomplish this. After all, in 2004, the cover of SLAM magazine featured high school All-American Shaun Livingston standing next to other NBA draft stand-outs with the declaration "Ready or not... Here they come!"[101] But Livingston's path

---

100 "Cleveland Cavaliers at Golden State Warriors Box Score, June 2, 2016." Basketball Reference. Last modified 2019. Accessed May 31, 2019. https://www.basketball-reference.com/boxscores/201606020GSW.html.

101 SLAM Magazine. *Ready or Not ... Here They Come*. Image. Accessed May 31, 2019. https://vignette.wikia.nocookie.net/slammagazine/images/b/b7/SLAM80.jpg/revision/latest?cb=20130203072929.

to a game-saving 20 points in the NBA Finals in a game when the high-octane Golden State Warriors needed him the most against LeBron James was a rocky road. It was an unpredictable path that featured one of the most grotesque recorded sports injuries of all time.

February 26, 2007. Coming off a breakaway fast-break steal against the Charlotte Bobcats, Shaun Livingston navigated around the one Bobcat in his way and rose up for a wide-open layup. As the ball rolled off of the rim, Livingston's left leg planted awkwardly, and he landed with full force directly on top of it. As his leg folded under the weight of his own body, it snapped. As the players came down the other end of the court, Livingston screamed in pain.[102] "My leg was deformed," he recalls. "My knee joint was dislocated and out of place. It was painful. 10 seconds felt like an hour. It was only like 10-15 seconds. But until they put my knee back into place, it was excruciating for sure."[103]

As Livingston was rushed to the hospital, it was discovered that he tore his anterior cruciate ligament (ACL), posterior

---

102 "WORST NBA Injury EVER? Doctor Explains Shaun Livingston Injury." Video file. YouTube. Posted by Brian Sutterer, December 22, 2018. Accessed May 31, 2019. https://www.youtube.com/watch?v=Et4Nqu3vAtg.

103 Spears, Marc J. "Can't Be Defeated: The Shaun Livingston Story." The Undefeated. Last modified May 17, 2016. Accessed May 31, 2019. https://theundefeated.com/features/never-defeated-the-shaun-livingston-story/.

cruciate ligament (PCL), and medial cruciate ligament (MCL). His lateral cruciate ligament (LCL) was intact. Of these four knee ligaments, if two or more are torn, it is likely that the knee will become dislocated, which was the case in Livingston's injury. The main artery responsible for supplying blood to the lower leg is in line with the femur and tibia – the bones that comprise the knee joint. As a result, major knee dislocations can possibly require amputations due to a cutoff of blood flow. However, because doctors were able to push Livingston's knee back into place on the floor at the game, he was able to maintain blood flow in his lower leg, which allowed for doctors to save his leg in the surgery that followed.[104]

A reconstruction of Livingston's knee was performed by Dr. James Andrews, who Livingston recalls told him, "It [is] a mountain to climb … but there was never a closed door on [your] career."[105] After surgery, Livingston recalls, "The knee was all deformed, bloodied up and leaking with pus. I just couldn't move it. Stiff. It was like I had a spare leg. All of my quad was skinny. It was like a pole with a pineapple in the

---

104 "WORST NBA Injury EVER? Doctor Explains Shaun Livingston Injury." Video file. YouTube. Posted by Brian Sutterer, December 22, 2018. Accessed May 31, 2019. https://www.youtube.com/watch?v=Et4Nqu3vAtg.

105 Zillgitt, Jeff. "How Shaun Livingston found NBA life after ugly injury." USA Today. Last modified March 20, 2014. Accessed May 31, 2019. https://www.usatoday.com/story/sports/nba/nets/2014/03/20/shaun-livingston-return-knee-injury-brooklyn/6655413/.

middle of it."[106] Livingston endured a 20-month recovery following his surgery. As he constantly worked with physical therapists on exercises that aimed to strengthen his reconstructed knee, Livingston had a newfound feeling of purpose. He recalls, "As I was starting to come back into the NBA … I felt like my purpose was to inspire people to get through hard times and struggle. I felt like that was a higher calling and [a] bigger purpose, rather than who I was supposed to be as a player."[107]

As Livingston worked himself into better shape, he also faced a significant mental hurdle. "The mental hurdle is the hardest part." claims Livingston. "You've got to get behind the wheel after that car accident."[108] Livingston credits putting in work during rehab for empowering himself to get into game shape mentally and physically. Livingston proudly declares, "That's a testament to God and all the work that I put in and

106 Spears, Marc J. "Can't Be Defeated: The Shaun Livingston Story." The Undefeated. Last modified May 17, 2016. Accessed May 31, 2019. https://theundefeated.com/features/never-defeated-the-shaun-livingston-story/.

107 Ibid

108 Coro, Paul. "Shaun Livingston's career nearly ended with a grotesque knee injury. Instead he's a two-time NBA champion seeking another title." Los Angeles Times. Last modified April 13, 2018. Accessed May 31, 2019.https://www.latimes.com/sports/nba/la-sp-nba-playoffs-livingston-20180413-story.html.

everyone that I worked with. Physically, I don't even think about it."[109]

After his bounce back from one of the most notorious sports injuries of all time, Livingston is also a believer in the importance of preventative medicine. Livingston explains, "With my rehab now I'm well versed with how the body reacts and having symptoms. I try to stay ahead of the curve."[110] To this day, Livingston stays in NBA shape with exercises that target his quadriceps, calves, and glutes to provide extra support to his knee. According to Livingston, the constant training helps immensely. "It's just kind of ironic with how I came into the NBA, with all the expectations. You would've thought coming in the way I did that my career would last long. You'd think I'd have my more peak years in the beginning or middle. Mine just came a little later. For the last six years, I've felt the best."[111] Livingston views his injury as a wake-up call to take better care of his body and take

109 Zillgitt, Jeff. "How Shaun Livingston found NBA life after ugly injury." USA Today. Last modified March 20, 2014. Accessed May 31, 2019. https://www.usatoday.com/story/sports/nba/nets/2014/03/20/shaun-livingston-return-knee-injury-brooklyn/6655413/.

110 Spears, Marc J. "Can't Be Defeated: The Shaun Livingston Story." The Undefeated. Last modified May 17, 2016. Accessed May 31, 2019. https://theundefeated.com/features/never-defeated-the-shaun-livingston-story/.

111 Coro, Paul. "Shaun Livingston's career nearly ended with a grotesque knee injury. Instead he's a two-time NBA champion seeking another title." Los Angeles Times. Last modified April 13, 2018. Accessed May 31, 2019. https://www.latimes.com/sports/nba/la-sp-nba-playoffs-livingston-20180413-story.html.

preventative exercise more seriously. According to him, "It's like a gift and a curse. To have those injuries at a young age … if it's not career-ending it's a gift because it gives you that awareness like … 'I've really got to take care of my body.' As you get older, you see changes happening and beat them to the punch."[112]

To cap off an already miraculous comeback, Livingston has enjoyed a long, successful NBA career. He was a crucial piece that helped the Golden State Warriors secure the 2015, 2017, and 2018 NBA titles in arguably the best dynasty in basketball has ever seen. Livingston looks back at his career and his late-career success with bliss, saying, "I won the championship … There were times I just wanted to make the playoffs."[113]

---

112 Ibid

113 Spears, Marc J. "Can't Be Defeated: The Shaun Livingston Story." The Undefeated. Last modified May 17, 2016. Accessed May 31, 2019. https://theundefeated.com/features/never-defeated-the-shaun-livingston-story/.

CHAPTER 7

LEBRON JAMES: CHOSEN·1

———

A knee contusion, a pinkie sprain, ankle sprains, a cheekbone fracture, a pectoral strain, a hamstring strain, a rib contusion, a shin contusion, the flu, a sprained big toe, knee tendinitis, back spasms, LASIK eye surgery, a shoulder contusion, a sprained index finger, big toe soreness, a benign parotid gland tumor, a wrist contusion, a quadricep contusion, an elbow bone bruise, hamstring cramps, a head cold, an elbow contusion, a dislocated ring finger, leg cramps, knee tightness, back soreness, a groin strain, a broken nose, ankle soreness, shoulder soreness, more ankle sprains, more back spasms, more quadricep contusions, more leg cramps, lower back tightness, another head cold, more knee pain.[114]

This laundry list of injuries seems like it could perhaps belong to an athlete whose career was tragically cut short by injuries. The fractures, contusions, cramps, strains, and soreness from head to big toe might suggest that the body they appear on belongs to an old veteran athlete, nearing the end of their prime and contemplating retirement. It's hard to imagine that these injuries have all been sustained by someone who is still very much in the midst of their prime. It's hard to wrap your head around the fact that the athlete who has sustained all these injuries has been the consensus best player alive in their sport for at least the past decade. It's nearly impossible to perceive that the man whose injury history is listed above is debatably the most durable professional athlete in history. Believe it or not, this medical history belongs to the seemingly invincible LeBron James.

For the entire duration of the 2010s, LeBron James has been at the forefront of the NBA. In fact, James was at the center of the basketball universe many years prior to the 2003 season in which he was drafted first overall by the Cleveland Cavaliers.

114 Stotts, Jeff. "An In-Depth Look at the Injury History of LeBron James." In Street Clothes. Last modified January 1, 2015. Accessed May 31, 2019. http://instreetclothes.com/2015/01/01/depth-look-injury-history-lebron-james/.

In February 2002, the 16-year-old from Akron, Ohio appeared on the cover of Sports Illustrated magazine. "The Chosen One," read the cover, featuring James in his St. Vincent-St. Mary varsity high school jersey, rocking a green headband and holding a yellow basketball right next to his face, which was replete with youthful enthusiasm.[115] This teenager from Akron was touted as the heir to Michael Jordan with the once-in-a-generation talent to change the game forever.

In 2003, as an 18-year-old phenom, James averaged 20.9 points, 5.5 rebounds, and 5.9 assists as he took the league by storm.[116] 2003 was also the year I started watching basketball seriously. My dad and grandpa had been watching games in our living room after dinner for as long as I could remember, but for the first time, as a wide-eyed five-year-old, I took the initiative to turn on the TV and flip to ESPN. And almost instantly, I fell in love with the game of basketball. I fell in love with watching LeBron James play basketball.

As he took home Rookie of the Year honors, LeBron James was quickly showing doubters that he deserved the "Chosen·1"

115 "2002 LeBron James Sports Illustrated First Issue No Label." Bonanza. Accessed May 31, 2019. https://www.bonanza.com/listings/2002-Lebron-James-Sports-Illustrated-First-Issue-No-Label/659844193?goog_pla=1&gpid=293946777986&keyword=&goog_pla=1&pos=104&ad_type=pla&gclid=CjwKCAiA3vfgBRB9EiwAkfpd3D9gaMCc97nc6ZRbsFQOQ78vV59TxJ4NR0VohsE6DifJtcU5k6iCh
116 NBA. "LeBron James." NBA Advanced Stats. Last modified 2019. Accessed May 31, 2019. https://stats.nba.com/player/2544/.

tattoo he had inked across his back. James had put Cleveland on the map and the league on notice. He had lived up to the hype. By his third season, James was averaging well over 31 points per game and leading the Cavaliers on deep playoff runs, putting the team on his back to close game after game.[117]

In his sixth season, James won his first MVP award. The following year, James was again named MVP of the league.[118] One thing that still eluded the best player on the planet was an NBA championship. Despite spending year after year mounting playoff runs, the LeBron James-led Cavaliers always fell short of the ultimate goal of capturing the championship ring that had eluded the franchise since its inception.

As LeBron fell short of this ultimate goal once again in the 2009-10 season and made the move to South Beach to play on the Miami Heat with close friends and fellow 2003 draft class superstars Dwyane Wade and Chris Bosh, he became the villain of the NBA. After James made what has become known infamously as "The Decision," he continued his unmatched level of play. In his time with the Heat, James took home two more MVP awards. James also led the Heat

---

117 NBA. "LeBron James." NBA Advanced Stats. Last modified 2019. Accessed May 31, 2019. https://stats.nba.com/player/2544/.

118 "NBA MVP Award Winners." NBA. Last modified 2019. Accessed May 31, 2019. http://www.nba.com/history/awards/mvp.

to four consecutive NBA Finals appearances, securing his first two NBA titles and NBA Finals MVP awards.

Prior to the 2014 season, with another major free agency decision looming, LeBron took to Sports Illustrated with three simple words: "I'm coming home."[119] As James took his family back to where it all started, it was clear he had unfinished business at home in Cleveland. With James back at the helm, the Cavaliers made the NBA Finals four years in a row. All four times, they took on the Golden State Warriors dynasty. Although the Warriors, led by Stephen Curry, claimed three of these four titles, LeBron James fulfilled his prophecy in the 2015-16 season.

In the 2015-16 season, the Golden State Warriors finished the regular season with a record of 73-9 — the best record in NBA history. As the Warriors burned through the rest of the Western Conference and to the NBA Finals, LeBron dragged a severely under-matched Cavaliers squad through the East. As the Warriors took a 3-1 stranglehold over the Cavs, the James-led team seemed out of luck. No team had ever come back from a 3-1 deficit in the NBA Finals. Then again, not every team had LeBron James.

---

119 Florjancic, Matthew. "'I'm coming home': Revisit LeBron James' infamous letter." WKYC3. Last modified June 20, 2016. Accessed May 31, 2019. https://www.wkyc.com/article/sports/nba/cavaliers/im-coming-home-revisit-lebron-james-infamous-letter/250422956.

41 points, 16 rebounds, 7 assists, 3 steals, 3 blocks. That's what it took from LeBron for the Cavaliers to pull out a Game Five win on the road in Oakland.[120] Following up that effort? 41 points, 8 rebounds, 11 assists, 4 steals, and 3 blocks to squeak by the Warriors in Cleveland.[121] LeBron was putting up greatest-of-all-time type numbers, willing the massive underdog Cavaliers to victory. The stage was set for a Game Seven showdown at the Warriors' home court, Oracle Arena.

With a little over four minutes remaining in the final game of the playoffs, the Cavaliers and Warriors were deadlocked at 89 apiece. As time ticked down, neither team could break the tie. With two minutes remaining, the score was still even, 89 to 89. Then, as Andre Iguodala stole a pass from the Cavaliers' side of the court, triggering a fast break the other way, a Warriors bucket to pull ahead seemed inevitable. As Iguodala passed the half-court line, he gunned a past to Steph Curry. With only Cavs guard J.R. Smith back to defend, Curry immediately bounced the ball back to Iguodala, who was now racing by the free-throw line. As Iguodala gathered the ball strongly with both of his massive arms, he leapt, contorting his body around Smith easily with his hand right by

---

120 "Cleveland Cavaliers at Golden State Warriors Box Score, June 13, 2016."Basketball Reference. Last modified 2019. Accessed May 31, 2019. https://www.basketball-reference.com/boxscores/201606130GSW.html.

121 "Golden State Warriors at Cleveland Cavaliers Box Score, June 16, 2016." Basketball Reference. Last modified 2019. Accessed May 31, 2019. https://www.basketball-reference.com/boxscores/201606160CLE.html.

the glass for an easy layup. Suddenly, LeBron James skied in out of nowhere. As he took off from just inside the free-throw line, he met Iguodala at the backboard, slapping the ball off of the backboard, well above the rim.[122]

According to teammate Richard Jefferson, "The last time I saw [LeBron James] move at 100%? It's like, you see it happening and you're watching the ball and I literally see a black blur. He gets the block and you're like 'Huh? What?' but I had still never seen anybody move that fast, to the point that it's a blur."[123]

Fired up by James' late-game heroics, the Cavaliers went on to secure a victory, with Kyrie Irving hitting an iconic step-back three-pointer over Steph Curry and James icing the game at the free throw line. James broke into tears, celebrating the Cavaliers' first championship with his teammates. As he made his way over to reporter Doris Burke, donning a championship hat and pulling a championship t-shirt over his sweat-covered forearms, James was visibly shaken. Burke asked if he could describe how he was feeling.

122 "LeBron James' Historic Block on Andre Iguodala From All Angles." Video file. YouTube. Posted by NBA, June 21, 2016. Accessed May 31, 2019. https://www.youtube.com/watch?v=-zd62MxKXp8.
123 Gonzalez, Eddie. "LeBron's Legendary Block Is Somehow Even Better When Told From Richard Jefferson's Point Of View." Uproxx. Last modified March 23, 2017. Accessed May 31, 2019. https://uproxx.com/dimemag/lebron-block-finals-richard-jefferson-retelling-podcast-video/.

Almost instantaneously, James replied, "I set out a goal two years, when I came back to bring a championship to this city. I gave everything that I have. I put my heart, my blood, my sweat, my tears to this game and…" Choking back tears, he continued, "And, against all odds, against all odds, I don't know why we want to take the hardest road, I don't know why the man above gives me the hardest road, but it's nothing the man above don't put you in situations you can't handle, and I just kept that same positive attitude, like, instead of saying 'why me,' saying 'this is what he want me to do.'" As he looked at the camera, LeBron yelled, "CLEVELAND! THIS IS FOR YOU!"[124]

LeBron James' 3-1 comeback rehashed the greatest-of-all-time debate I had with my dad, and my parents added "never disrespect Michael Jordan" to the list of house rules. In the two seasons that followed, although they made the NBA Finals with LeBron James' continued dominance, the Cavaliers were no match for the Warriors, who added super-star Kevin Durant to an already stacked roster. Despite the disappointing endings of the 2016 and 2017 seasons for the Cavs, both seasons were periods of unforeseen improvement in James' game.

---

124 NBC Sports. "LeBron: 'Cleveland this is for you.'" Video file. NBC Sports Philadelphia. Accessed May 31, 2019. https://www.nbcsports.com/philadelphia/video/lebron-james-cleveland-you.

In the 2016 season, James set a career high, with 8.6 rebounds per game and 8.7 assists per game to go with his usual 26.4 points per game. At the age of 32. In his 14th season. In the following 2017 season, James matched his career-high rebounding average with 8.6 per game while setting a new career high for assists per game with 9.1. He also scored a huge 27.5 points per game. And for the first time in his career, he played in all 82 regular season games while leading the league in minutes per game.[125] [126]

LeBron James was already the best player on the planet, the greatest small forward to ever play the game of basketball, a four-time MVP, a three-time NBA Champion, a three-time NBA Finals MVP. A lock for the GOAT (greatest of all time) discussion. But he was still getting better as a 33-year-old in his 15th season in the NBA. This was unheard of and almost impossible. In his 15th season in the NBA, his last before retiring from the game for good, Michael Jordan was averaging only 20.0 points per game to go with 6.1 rebounds per game and 3.8 assists per game.[127] At a time when his game was supposed to be declining as his mileage began to catch

125 NBA. "LeBron James." NBA Advanced Stats. Last modified 2019. Accessed May 31, 2019. https://stats.nba.com/player/2544/.
126 "2017-2018 NBA Season Leaders." ESPN. Last modified 2019. Accessed May 31, 2019. http://www.espn.com/nba/seasonleaders/_/league/nba/sort/avgMinutes/year/2018.
127 "Michael Jordan." ESPN. Last modified 2019. Accessed May 31, 2019. http://www.espn.com/nba/player/stats/_/id/1035/michael-jordan.

up to him, LeBron James defied all odds. He was progressing instead of regressing. This whole time, the world had thought it was watching peak LeBron James when in reality, no one had really seen peak LeBron James. But how is this possible? What is the secret behind the reign of dominance King James has held over the league, which has no end in the foreseeable future? It all starts with LeBron's medical team.

From the start, taking care of his body was a major priority for LeBron James. According to Keith Dambrot, LeBron's high school coach, "He knew he was going to play a lot of minutes and that people were going to beat him up. He knew that his body would take tremendous wear and tear, so he started working on this years ago."[128] This dedication to caring for his body was apparent in his rookie season. As described by then-Cavaliers assistant Stephen Silas, "He didn't look like any rookie I've ever seen before. His athleticism that accompanied that great body was unbelievable; something I've never seen before and haven't seen since."[129]

---

128 Cassilo, David. "What's the Secret to LeBron James' Athletic Invincibility?" Bleacher Report. Last modified October 10, 2016. Accessed May 31, 2019. https://bleacherreport.com/articles/2661150-whats-the-secret-to-lebron-james-athletic-invincibility.

129 Cassilo, David. "What's the Secret to LeBron James' Athletic Invincibility?" Bleacher Report. Last modified October 10, 2016. Accessed May 31, 2019. https://bleacherreport.com/articles/2661150-whats-the-secret-to-lebron-james-athletic-invincibility.

According to Mike Miller, an NBA sharpshooter who played with James during his Miami days, "It's all about longevity. People are investing a lot of money in this, and they want that product to be out there a long time. These guys are billionaires for a reason, and they don't want their investment to get hurt. They now put their investment in training. Where a lot of people don't do it, he puts a lot of money behind taking care of his body. A lot of people think it's a big expense, but that big expense has allowed him to make a lot more money for a long period of time. He continues to play 40 minutes a night, and the ball is in his hands at all times. It's ridiculous."[130] LeBron James' unique view of care for his body as an investment rather than a simple expense has enabled him to spend whatever is required to afford the cutting edge in recovery and preventative sports medicine. In fact, according to Malcolm Gladwell, a groundbreaking author who spoke about a conversation with James' business partner Maverick Carter, "And [Maverick Carter's] like, 'well, he's replicated the gym that whatever team – whether it was Miami or Cleveland—he's replicated all the equipment they have in the team's gym in his house. He has two trainers. Everywhere he goes, he has a trainer with him.' I'm paraphrasing what he told me, so I might not be getting all these facts right. He's got chefs. He has all the science of how to sleep. All these different things. Masseuses. Everything he

---

130 Ibid

does in his life is constructed to have him play basketball and to stay on the court and to be as healthy as possible and to absorb punishment when he goes in to the basket and he gets crushed by people." The price tag for all of these accommodations to ensure his body is firing on all cylinders? Around $1.5 million per year.[131] More than some NBA players' annual salaries.

James' approach towards maintaining his peak performance and preventing injuries is holistic. As phrased by Kevin Durant, an NBA champion and a longtime friend of James, "One thing I learned about LeBron — I worked out with him — LeBron takes care of his body. He knows that in order for him to play that long, his body has to be up. He has to keep that in shape. Like, he works on his body, like, religiously."[132] Former teammate Iman Shumpert describes James' treatment of his health as a priority, stating, "He just takes care of his body. He's got his trainers there. He put ice on right after the game — he gonna sit there. Like, people may think it's diva-ish, but that man will get his treatment and be late. 'I'll be late to this event, even though y'all paid me all this

131 Simmons, Bill. "LeBron James's Life Is Constructed to Keep Him on the Court." The Ringer. Last modified June 8, 2016. Accessed May 31, 2019.https://www.theringer.com/2016/6/8/16040612/ nba-lebron-james-bill-simmons-malcolm-gladwell-5369d6959c67.

132 Davis, Scott. "LeBron James takes immaculate care of his body, and the NBA world is in awe of it." Business Insider. Last modified June 3, 2018. Accessed May 31, 2019. https://www.businessinsider.com/ lebron-james-body-care-workouts-diet-insane-2017-10.

money to be here. Because I gotta do everything I gotta do to make sure I preserve my body so I can do this tomorrow.'"[133]

The hidden hero in all of this? LeBron's trainer Mike Mancias, a fitness guru who prefers to stay behind the scenes. For Mancias, it's all about keeping the focus on his coworkers and the athletes. In his own words, "It's not about me. I'm a chef at a restaurant. I don't own my own restaurant. Without doing all the social media and pictures, I still get attention. My brand, if you will, is making sure we're in the right position to win championships, not just mak[ing] me famous." Mancias has been helping James for his entire 16-year career. Their relationship has grown over the years, and according to Mancias, "[James is] family, and it goes beyond basketball and beyond anything on the hardwood. He trusts me and I trust him, so it's all good."[134]

Although Mancias was employed by the Cleveland Cavaliers during James' first stint with the team, James worked with Mancias privately as well. These private sessions on James' own coin were supported by the Cavaliers, and

---

133 Davis, Scott. "LeBron James takes immaculate care of his body, and the NBA world is in awe of it." Business Insider. Last modified June 3, 2018. Accessed May 31, 2019. https://www.businessinsider.com/lebron-james-body-care-workouts-diet-insane-2017-10.

134 Bishara, Motez. "LeBron James: Keeping a billion-dollar body in shape." CNN. Last modified December 13, 2017. Accessed May 31, 2019. https://www.cnn.com/2017/12/13/sport/lebron-james-physical-trainer-mike-mancias-cleveland-cavs/ index.html.

Mancias credits communication as the key factor that allowed him to work so closely with James at the onset of his professional career. According to Mancias, "These teams, these owners, these general managers, they are the ones investing millions upon millions of dollars in these players' contracts, and so we want to make sure that they are in the right hands of someone with knowledgeable credentials. I think all teams, to be honest with you, would prefer that players stick to their own strength coaches or athletic trainers, but we're in a day and age where every player on the bench can hire a personal trainer for the summer basically to be on call 24/7. It's a lot easier, and there is a comfort level as well when you have your own guy. Everyone wants individual attention, individual care, and I don't blame them."[135]

James' individual care continued as he made the move from Cleveland to Miami. As James made a transition into the next part of his career, so did Mancias. Mancias also left the Cavaliers' training staff and was on James' payroll until he was officially hired as a trainer by the Miami Heat the following year. Throughout this transition, Mancias made sure the focus was on James, not himself, in true hidden hero fashion. "I'm not here to be a sideshow," Mancias recalled, "Things went really smoothly because we all communicated, and I

---

135 Ibid

was on the same page. It was about winning championships for him, not for me."[136]

After James' time with the Miami Heat had come to an end and he moved back home to Cleveland, Mancias came with him, securing a job with the Cavaliers, who were glad to see him and his number one client return to the team. After James made the move to the Los Angeles Lakers prior to the 2018-19 NBA season, Mancias left the Cavaliers.[137] He continues to loyally work with James, keeping him firing on all cylinders as he carries a young Lakers team towards a playoff run.

For James, taking care of his body is more than a full-time job. In fact, LeBron says, "It's every day. Around the clock every single day, working on my body. Either with treatment or working on my body in the weight room. Continuing to just build strength throughout the season when everybody else is kind of tearing down ... not putting too much pounding on my legs when I'm on the court but being very efficient. I've kind of figured that out."[138]

---

136 Ibid

137 Gundersen, Erik García. "Two staff members with strong LeBron ties have left the Cavaliers." LeBronWire. Last modified July 20, 2018. Accessed May 31, 2019. https://lebronwire.usatoday.com/2018/07/20/two-staff-members-with-strong-lebron-ties-have-left-the-cavaliers/.

138 Davis, Scott. "LeBron James takes immaculate care of his body, and the NBA world is in awe of it." Business Insider. Last modified June 3, 2018. Accessed May 31, 2019. https://www.businessinsider.com/lebron-james-body-care-workouts-diet-insane-2017-10.

The part of James' seemingly perfect basketball body that has given him the most trouble in his career is his back. Mancias recalls James complaining about back soreness back when James was only 21 years old. In 2015, the seemingly invincible James took off two weeks during the regular season to work on rehabilitating his sore back, which was giving him mobility issues on the court. James received anti-inflammatory injections in his back to help manage the swelling and pain, and at the time, the Cavaliers deemed it necessary for him to step away from the court to focus on resting and rehabbing the back that was so used to carrying the entire team. James and Mancias turned to core strengthening exercises.[139] They can be spotted in arenas hours before games, James incredulously balancing himself on a yoga bubble and tossing medicine balls back and forth with Mancias. James continues to do hip stabilization exercises, which help to keep his back in check.

Mancias and James work together with immaculate precision. After an NBA Finals game, when James is truly playing at 100%, the recovery process consists of everything from simple techniques that anyone can employ at home to futuristic techniques that only the most elite athletes are likely to take

139 Windhorst, Brian. "How LeBron James fixed his back and is on track to play all 82 games." ESPN. Last modified March 19, 2018. Accessed May 31, 2019.http://www.espn.com/nba/story/_/id/22778062/how-lebron-james-fixed-back-track-play-all-82-games-nba.

advantage of. Right off the bat, James hops in an ice bath, which helps calibrate his central nervous system, shifting his body from activity mode to recovery mode. Additionally, James drinks hydrating beverages prepared by Mancias, which contain high-carbohydrate recovery fluids mixed with water.[140] These beverages are designed to increase James' glycogen levels. Glycogen is a complex carbohydrate found in muscles and the liver, and it is used by the human body to store energy. This energy reserve is broken down into glucose when it needs to be used. James' recovery beverages are crucial in ensuring he is ready to go for the strenuous games to come in the very near future.

Travel is an additional hurdle for professional athletes. According to Garry Vitti, a former strength and conditioning coach for the Los Angeles Lakers, "One is the physical exertion that they just put out for the game, and the other part is the travel because now they're changing locations." During the NBA Finals, flights are a frequent nuisance as games shift from one city to another. When LeBron has to fly, dealing with the altitude is a notable issue because experiencing flying altitudes tends to increase swelling and dehydration. To combat this unwanted side effect of jet travel, James ensures he wears

---

140 Berger, Ken. "How trainer gets spent LeBron James from one Herculean effort to next." CBS Sports. Last modified June 10, 2015. Accessed May 31, 2019.https://www.cbssports.com/nba/news/how-trainer-gets-spent-lebron-james-from-one-herculean-effort-to-next/.

compression tights under his pants to prevent increased swelling. Additionally, James follows Mancias' fine-tuned diet plan for air travel, which consists of constantly hydrating and eating complex proteins and carbohydrates. As he sits on the plane, an electro-stimulation machine is used to consistently contract LeBron's muscles and foster the flushing of toxins such as lactic acid, a byproduct of strenuous exercise, from his entire body. To aid with this flushing process, James is typically hooked up to large compression boots that apply pressure to his legs by filling with air and promote circulation. Mancias also gives James soft-tissue massages to continue to flush lactic acid from his muscles, which further allows for his muscles to rebuild with the protein and carbohydrates he consumed. After they land, James goes to work on a stationary bike before taking hot-cold contrast baths and resting. The day before a game, Mancias typically works with James for around four hours, providing him more of his perfected treatment, massage, and rehabilitation training. On the day of the game, Mancias works with James on parts of his body that are still particularly achy, such as his back.[141]

LeBron James fully credits his trainer with getting him ready for important NBA Finals games. After Game Two of the

---

141 Berger, Ken. "How trainer gets spent LeBron James from one Herculean effort to next." CBS Sports. Last modified June 10, 2015. Accessed May 31, 2019.https://www.cbssports.com/nba/news/how-trainer-gets-spent-lebron-james-from-one-herculean-effort-to-next/.

2015 Finals, James said, "That's why I've got one of the best trainers in the world in Mike Mancias, who will make sure I'm ready for Game Three. I'll be ready. There's not much recovery time. Just getting my body as close as I can to 100 percent. I still have a lot of time right now throughout the day to stay on the treatment regimen I've been on. ... When you only have a day or 36 hours, you've got to cram everything in there. Hopefully the body reacts accordingly to it." And for James, it almost always reacts exactly how he wants it to.[142]

LeBron James was placed in the limelight of the basketball world at the age of 16 as he graced the cover of Sports Illustrated magazine. As the most hype-generating youth athlete in the history of sports, he found a way to do the unimaginable as he exceeded the hype. An 18-year-old James famously told the world, "There's no pressure. There's no pressure at all. I've been getting pressure since I was 10 years old. I'm doing something that I love to do. And that's play the game of basketball. Y'all like to watch me play basketball."[143] And we've had the privilege of watching him play his beautiful brand of basketball over the past two decades due to his hard work and dedication and that of his medical and training team. The perfect combination of freakish

142 Ibid

143 Estiler, Keith. "18-Year-Old LeBron James Predicts Future Success in Latest NikeVideo." Hypebeast. Last modified October 21, 2018. Accessed May 31, 2019. https://hypebeast.com/2018/10/lebron-james-nike-just-do-it-film.

God-given physical abilities, a deeply cerebral understanding of the game and himself, and an insatiable hunger for improvement through every means possible, James continues to play at the same high level that other superstars before him have been unable to maintain. LeBron has certainly lived up to the billing as the Chosen One, and after 16 years of dominance followed by a move to the storied Los Angeles Lakers, the best version of LeBron James may be yet to come.

CHAPTER 8

ADRIAN PETERSON: BEING THE GREATEST

———

"9 yards. Boy, that's gotta hurt," sighed ESPN sideline reporter Josina Anderson as she spoke to Adrian Peterson after the Minnesota Vikings' Week 17 bout against the Green Bay Packers. "9 yards what? 9 yards what, from breaking it?" replied the stud running back, with a stoic look on his face. "That's what I heard," replied Anderson, shaking her head, visibly disappointed that Peterson had fallen just short of breaking the single-season rushing yards record. Instantly, Peterson also referred to by his initials "AP" and the letters "AD" (standing for "All Day") – replied, "Oh. Well, you know ultimately, we got the W. And that was my main focus coming into the game. I said, 'if it happens then it happens, but don't focus on it.'"[144] The Vikings needed to win this game, and behind AP's 199 rushing yards on 34 attempts and two total touchdowns, they punched their ticket to the playoffs. As Peterson was an easy choice for MVP of the 2012 season, finishing the year with a career high 2,097 rushing yards and 13 total touchdowns, the discussion surrounding the running back now centered around whether or not he was the greatest rusher of all time.[145] However, a little over eight months before the season started, the discussion around AD was whether he would ever return to an NFL field.

On December 24, 2011, as the Vikings took on the Washington Redskins, Peterson took a carry up the middle from the Vikings' 10-yard line when his planted left leg was drilled from the left side by a defender. As Peterson hit the ground, he drove his right foot into the turf and sunk his helmet into the grass in agony as the training staff swarmed around him. As he was carted off of the field, he tried his best to hide any indication that he was in pain, tossing his football gloves to a fan in the crowd while remaining his usual cool and collected

144 "Adrian Peterson goes for Eric Dickerson's rushing record - 2012 Week 17 Vikings vs. Packers." Video file. YouTube. Posted by NFL, July 21, 2015. Accessed May 31, 2019. https://www.youtube.com/watch?v=WVkEIydlmFA.

145 "Adrian Peterson." Pro Football Reference. Last modified 2019. Accessed May 31, 2019. https://www.pro-football-reference.com/players/P/PeteAd01/gamelog/2012/.

self.[146] As MRIs confirmed Adrian Peterson had torn his anterior cruciate ligament (ACL) and medial collateral ligament (MCL), many sportswriters were sure they had seen the last of the All-Pro running back. Shockingly, Peterson was not too worried about himself. He recalled, "You've got to have one believer. I'm sure there weren't many out there, but I definitely believed I could come back and be better than I was before."

When Peterson hit the finely cut grass, he immediately knew something major had just transpired. "I knew I had torn something. I didn't know exactly what it was. At the moment, it was just unbearable, and probably the worst pain I have felt." As he got off the field, Peterson recalls, "I remember telling myself then, 'you gotta bounce back from this.'" Six days after the catastrophic injury, Peterson had his ACL arthroscopically reconstructed by Dr. James Andrews. Most ACL reconstruction surgeries are conducted weeks after the injury occurs; however, Peterson recalled, "I didn't have any increased risks at all because my knee really didn't swell. That was something that was shocking to the trainers and the doctors."[147] According to Dr. Andrews, Peterson "defied

146 "#1 Adrian Peterson: Torn ACL to Rushing for Over 2,000 yards | Top 10 Player Comebacks | NFL Films." Video file. YouTube. Posted by NFL Films, November 4, 2016. Accessed May 31, 2019. https://www.youtube.com/watch?v=ZWSY0jBe7yY.

147 "Adrian Peterson: Torn ACL was the worst pain ever." Video file. YouTube. Posted by Graham Bensinger, September 7, 2016. Accessed May 31, 2019. https://www.youtube.com/watch?v=JrdlxFY26cc&t=14s.

all odds." Dr. Andrews proclaimed, "If you operate on the right athlete, it makes you look pretty darn good as a physician. Adrian was that genetic athlete who could do what he's done."[148]

At the time, Adrian Peterson was the premier running back in all of football and arguably the best player in the NFL. Dr. Andrews did not allow that fact to generate any extra pressure for him and weigh him down. "You treat everybody as if they're special," Dr. Andrews states. "Don't do something out of the ordinary that is against your routine because they are some high-level athlete. Why do you have a routine? Because that is how you do it best. So, you don't change your routine if it's Adrian Peterson or somebody. Obviously there is more tension to that particular situation, but you have to fight that and try to stay within your boundaries. That kind of decision-making does not come early in your career, it comes later in your career. I just want to get this guy back so he can play. You start to get into trouble when you start to worry about, 'is the fate of this guy in my hands?'"

After successfully performing an arthroscopic knee surgery on Adrian Peterson, Dr. Andrews recalls telling him, "Hey

148 Wilson, Ryan. "Dr. Andrews on Adrian Peterson's recovery: 'He has defied the odds.'" CBS Sports. Last modified January 4, 2013. Accessed May 31, 2019. https://www.cbssports.com/nfl/news/dr-andrews-on-adrian-petersons-recovery-he-has-defied-the-odds/.

man, you're fixed. Go after it."[149] And Peterson went after it, putting every ounce of his physical and mental energy into rehabilitating his knee. Peterson recalls, "for me the easy part was just doing the work. Like, the first six weeks were hard because I really couldn't do anything. But the surgery was more rough because of the pain and the first couple of weeks of just going through that mentally." Peterson remembers the first two weeks after undergoing surgery as the toughest part of his injury, recalling, "during that time, the swelling was there, and you have increased pain and there were only one or two exercises I was able to do, you know, lifting your leg up just to keep the muscles working and firing. But that was the toughest time because during that time, you have all these thoughts that the weaker one throws in your direction and you bat them away and what not." Peterson claims his mental fortitude set him up to give his rehab everything he could, reminiscing, "If I were weak-minded, I could have easily gave in." As he battled negativity, Peterson recalled, "Those thoughts definitely crossed my mind, but I didn't let them sit them and build a house. They just passed through; I kept casting them down."[150] Peterson claims "The things

---

149 Pioneer Press. "Adrian Peterson's surgeon, James Andrews, says Vikings back 'has defied all odds.'" Twin Cities Pioneer Press. Last modified January 3, 2013. Accessed May 31, 2019. https://www.twincities.com/2013/01/03/adrian-petersons-surgeon-james-andrews-says-vikings-back-has-defied-all-odds/.

150 "Adrian Peterson: Torn ACL was the worst pain ever." Video file. YouTube. Posted by Graham Bensinger, September 7, 2016. Accessed May 31, 2019. https://www.youtube.com/watch?v=JrdlxFY26cc&t=14s.

you guys don't see is how much I work and grind and fought through different situations to get back. Mentally, I was able to push through when I was tired and didn't want to do anything. I definitely give credit to the things I put into my off-season."[151]

In the most crucial off-season of his career, Peterson's goal was clear. In an interview with ESPN reporter Josina Anderson, he famously declared, "I'm not trying to encounter no delays. First off, the ultimate goal is to come back 110% better than I was before. Be ready and available to play the first week of the regular season, that's my goal. Just to be able to help my team in any way I can to accomplish the ultimate goal: winning the NFC North title and helping us land a spot in the playoffs to accomplish the ultimate goal, which is winning a championship."[152] Peterson cited his lofty expectations of himself as the root allowing him to come back to the NFL so quickly. He declared the secret was "setting your standards to a point where no one would be able to catch up to you or surpass you."[153]

151 "Adrian Peterson: Torn ACL was the worst pain ever." Video file. YouTube. Posted by Graham Bensinger, September 7, 2016. Accessed May 31, 2019. https://www.youtube.com/watch?v=JrdlxFY26cc&t=14s.

152 "NFL: Peterson's road to recovery." Video file. YouTube. Posted by Espnamerica, May 20, 2012. Accessed May 31, 2019. https://www.youtube.com/watch?v=RCxPkvD-Y88.

153 Ibid

Peterson recalls that with the help of innovative ERMI's Flexion-ater and Extensionater, a rehabilitation device developed by Dr. Thomas Branch, his rehab process was greatly improved. The device allows patients to place one of their feet on a motile platform and stretch out their knee by operating a lever that causes the platform to slide. Peterson remembers, "It really helped me with my extension and getting my full range of motion back." Dr. Branch explains that the device allows strong tissues in the knee to stretch without allowing them to tear.[154]

Peterson also utilized the Nintendo Wii, a video game console, in his recovery. Peterson's medical team developed custom exercises for him that incorporated the Wii Balance Board and Wii Fit, which allowed him to get real-time feedback on his rehab.[155]

Peterson also used HydroWorx pools as a part of his rehabilitation as directed by Minnesota Vikings head athletic trainer Eric Sugarman. These pools feature treadmills and an automated system that changes the depth of the treadmill. Deeper water allows for greater buoyancy, allowing for more support for weak

154 "Adrian Peterson's recovery aided by ERMI Inc." Video file. YouTube. Posted by ERMI Inc, December 11, 2012. Accessed May 31, 2019. https://www.youtube.com/watch?v=YAI20FqF_38&t=1s.

155 Welch, Hanuman. "Minnesota Vikings' Adrian Peterson Uses Nintendo Wii for His Physical Therapy." Complex. Last modified August 12, 2012. Accessed May 31, 2019. https://www.complex.com/pop-culture/2012/08/minnesota-vikings-adrian-peterson-incorporates-wii-into-his-physical-therapy-regimen.

knees that are being rehabilitated. As Peterson continued with his rehabilitation process, the depth of the water was reduced as he became stronger. Peterson recalls, "Being able to get into the pool and put weight on [my knee], being able to run, to do things that at that point in time I wasn't able to do on the field, being able to run and do different drills inside the pool as far as lunges and doing things like that; I was able to strengthen my muscles and get back in my comfort zone."[156] Dr. James Andrews recalls, "Minnesota Vikings (Eric Sugarman) managed him perfectly. I sent Sugarman a text saying he should be very proud." According to Dr. Andrews, "Running backs don't come back within the first year like that in the NFL. They may come back and play a little bit. They don't do what he did. Nobody's ever done that if you look at the statistics of players returning to the NFL. We did a study. Running backs are the hardest to get back, period. The average NFL player … only about a little over 50 percent are still playing after two years. We say we have 90 to 90-plus percent success with (knee) surgeries (in non-NFL cases). But we're talking about playing in the NFL. It's not 90 percent, believe me."[157]

---

156 "Adrian Peterson's rapid recovery with HydroWorx pools." Video file. YouTube. Posted by HydroWorx International Inc., September 19, 2008. Accessed May 31, 2019. https://www.youtube.com/watch?v=k_40Rh984bI.

157 Pioneer Press. "Adrian Peterson's surgeon, James Andrews, says Vikings back 'has defied all odds.'" Twin Cities Pioneer Press. Last modified January 3, 2013. Accessed May 31, 2019. https://www.twincities.com/2013/01/03/adrian-petersons-surgeon-james-andrews-says-vikings-back-has-defied-all-odds/.

Adrian Peterson's recovery defied all odds, and he quickly became a symbol of the miraculous capabilities of the human body and modern medicine. According to Dr. Andrews, "The greatest revelation in sports medicine was in the 1970s, when the arthroscope was introduced. And we are still making advancements with minimally invasive techniques with the arthroscope." Peterson's incredible return to undisputed status as the best running back in football mere months after suffering an ACL tear caused a paradigm shift in sports at all levels. According to Dr. Sam Elguizaoui, a New York-based orthopedic surgeon specializing in minimally invasive arthroscopy and sports medicine, "In the NFL, six months is the fastest for an ACL injury. Adrian Peterson was one of those and he is a very unique case. When his case comes out, you have all these high school and college athletes come out and say, 'Peterson came back in 6 months,' but that is usually not how it goes. With my patients, I am telling them about eight months to a year conservatively for that person that is working hard but does not necessarily have the resources that the pro athletes have."

Adrian Peterson really only had one true goal over the course of his entire career, and it was the same goal that resonated in his head after he had suffered an injury that would have convinced most running backs of his age to hang up the pads for good: "Just to be the greatest." As AP returned to the NFL and shredded elite defense after elite defense en route to an

MVP performance, he also inspired an entire new wave of athletes to be steadfast as they faced seemingly insurmountable injuries. Like Adrian Peterson, so many athletes want to be the greatest, and thanks to him, they are inspired to work their way to excellence.

CHAPTER 9

PEYTON MANNING: LOVING YOUR JOB

———

"All right son, this one's over, good night," my dad muttered, slowly arising from the plush swivel chair. Knile Davis had just walked an 8-yard carry into the endzone, and the Chiefs were now up 24 to 17 in their 2015 Week Two divisional clash against the Broncos. With 2:27 left on the clock, I raised my eyebrows and glanced at my dad and before I could say anything, he lowered himself back into the plush red chair before blurting, "yeah, you're right, two minutes is way too much time to leave on the clock for him." And after a couple back-shoulder throws on the sidelines, the Broncos found themselves in the red zone with 40 seconds on the clock at 3rd and 10. As Manning yelled one of his classic Omahas and took the snap from the shotgun, he rocketed a pass to Emmanuel Sanders, who darted into the endzone with 35 seconds to spare.

The Broncos would go on to win the game in the last seconds on a fumble recovery for a touchdown, proving my dad right: two minutes was just way too much time to leave for Peyton Manning.[158] I smirked at my dad and teased, "I thought you were going to sleep." As he shook his head and again emerged out of his favorite chair, he smiled and said, "I've been watching Peyton do this since you were the size of a football." And with that, he was finally off to sleep.

The odds of getting to see that dumbfounded look on my dad's face after watching a 39-year-old throw lasers to close out that game were incredibly minute. In fact, Peyton Manning's renaissance in Denver seemed all but impossible a few years ago. In 2011, the Indianapolis Colts legend suffered from a herniated intervertebral disc that resulted in a pinched nerve in his neck, which seriously hindered his ability to throw a football. An injury like this typically occurs when the rigid outer layer of the disc becomes damaged and allows the soft inner layer to poke out and pinch a nerve. This injury is fairly common among athletes playing contact-heavy sports, but in Manning's case, it was particularly severe as he was experiencing weakness in his arm.[159] Surgery is the typical

---

158 "#4: Broncos vs. Chiefs (Week 2) | Top 20 Games of 2015 | NFL." Video file. YouTube. Posted by NFL, September 17, 2015. Accessed May 31, 2019. https://www.youtube.com/watch?v=Mt2u8TIKRCA.

159 Vaccaro, Alexander, and Gregory Schroeder. "Interest growing in Peyton Manning-like neck injuries in the NFL, MLB." Sports Illustrated. Last modified March 27, 2015. Accessed May 31, 2019. https://www.si.com/edge/2015/03/27/peyton-manning-neck-injury-rothman-denver-broncos.

intervention in cases as problematic as Manning's, and in May 2011, Manning was admitted to Northwestern Memorial Hospital in Chicago, where he underwent an anterior cervical discectomy and fusion. Surgeons removed a disc from his spine and then used a bone graft to fuse the vertebrae back together. This procedure reduced compression on the spinal cord and the roots of nerves in the cervical spine, which in turn stabilized the vertebrae that were giving him issues. Despite the successful surgery, Manning had a long, emotional, painful road ahead of him.[160]

As he first awoke from his deep anesthetically induced slumber, Manning did what anyone would do, attempting to push himself up. However, as he pushed his right hand into the mattress to hoist himself up, Manning's arm gave way and he fell right back onto the bed.[161] Terrifyingly, the right arm that had thrown for over 54,000 yards, won four MVP awards,

160 Jenkins, Sally. "Peyton Manning on his neck surgeries rehab — and how he almost didn't make it back." The Washington Post. Last modified October 21, 2013. Accessed May 31, 2019. https://www.washingtonpost.com/sports/redskins/peyton-manning-on-his-neck-surgeries-rehab--and-how-he-almost-didnt-make-it-back/2013/10/21/8e3b5ca6-3a55-11e3-b7ba-503fb5822c3e_story.html?noredirect=on&utm_term=.7d30e8dca503

161 Jenkins, Sally. "Peyton Manning on his neck surgeries rehab — and how he almost didn't make it back." The Washington Post. Last modified October 21, 2013. Accessed May 31, 2019. https://www.washingtonpost.com/sports/redskins/peyton-manning-on-his-neck-surgeries-rehab--and-how-he-almost-didnt-make-it-back/2013/10/21/8e3b5ca6-3a55-11e3-b7ba-503fb5822c3e_story.html?noredirect=on&utm_term=.7d30e8dca503

and brought home the Colts' only Lombardi Trophy of the 21st century now could not even support his own weight.[162] As Manning panicked and questioned the surgeon about the arm that paid his bills, the surgeon reassured him that the arm would take quite some time to return to normalcy, as was common in cases involving severe disc-related pinched nerves. Over the course of the following two weeks, Manning still felt as though his arm was weak, but he began to realize that his grip strength had also deteriorated. Manning recalls feeling, "If any other part of your body has some weakness you go, 'Well I can probably manage,' but when you're a quarterback and it's your right hand, you're certainly concerned as far as being able to do your job."[163] But Manning's ability to continue to do the job he had always grown up dreaming of doing seemed to be in grave jeopardy as he re-herniated the same compromised disc in his neck. At this point, Manning went back under the knife and out of the public eye.

A newly self-conscious Peyton Manning did everything he could to avoid the limelight, recalling, "I wasn't just going to throw with anybody around watching. I was guarded and protective." As he focused his attention towards the road to

162 "Peyton Manning." NFL. Last modified 2019. Accessed May 31, 2019. http://www.nfl.com/player/peytonmanning/2501863/careerstats.

163 Jenkins, Sally. "Peyton Manning on his neck surgeries rehab — and how he almost didn't make it back." The Washington Post. Last modified October 21, 2013. Accessed May 31, 2019. https://www.washingtonpost.com/sports/redskins/peyton-manning-on-his-neck-surgeries-rehab--and-how-he-almost-didnt-make-it-back/

recovery ahead, his path was complicated by an NFL labor lockout, which denied him access to the Colts' training staff or facilities. At this point, Manning was convinced by fellow Tennessee Volunteer and Colorado Rockies first baseman Todd Helton to make the move to Denver to rehab with the Rockies' veteran training staff. As Manning went down into the batting cage under Coors Field with Helton, ensuring complete secrecy, ready to throw a football for the first time since his neck surgeries, he took a deep breath. Manning cocked his arm back, ready to throw the ball to Helton who was standing a reasonable 10 yards away. As soon as he released the ball, Manning recalls, "the ball nose-dived after about five yards." As Helton chuckled and insisted "C'mon, quit kidding," a shocked Manning stared back blankly at him and murmured, "Man, I wish I was." It was quickly becoming clear that Manning's recovery was going to be more frustrating than he had initially anticipated.[164]

Manning's vertebrae injuries were compounded by a genetic background that he describes as "not picture-perfect." Peyton's older brother Cooper was diagnosed with spinal stenosis, the caving in of the spaces between vertebrae that leads to pressure being placed on the spinal cord, which ended his career as a wide receiver at the University of Mississippi. After witnessing Cooper's career being cut

---

164 Ibid

short by spinal stenosis, which left him wheelchair-bound for weeks, Archie Manning, the boys' father and former NFL quarterback, had Peyton and his younger brother Eli tested for potential spinal-cervical complications. Peyton was 16 years old at the time, and he was found to have a neck curvature that physicians said was not problematic enough to prohibit him from playing football at a high level, but it was something that could prove to be hazardous in the future. As this potential for complication was realized nearly twenty years after it had been identified, the work a 35-year-old Peyton Manning would have to put in if he ever wanted to step foot on a football field again seemed almost unmanageable. Manning decided to take a year off from football to focus on his recovery. Looking back, Manning said "I've never taken it for granted, ever since Cooper's career was taken from him just like that. So I always had it in perspective, and I didn't need a year off to remind me how lucky I was to play."[165]

The most frustrating part of the recovery process for Manning was that "there was no one to call who had this, no other thrower." Manning's medical team told him that nerve regeneration had a range of recovery anywhere from

---

165 Jenkins, Sally. "Peyton Manning on his neck surgeries rehab — and how he almost didn't make it back." The Washington Post. Last modified October 21, 2013. Accessed May 31, 2019. https://www.washingtonpost.com/sports/redskins/peyton-manning-on-his-neck-surgeries-rehab--and-how-he-almost-didnt-make-it-back/

0% to 100%, making it difficult to make any accurate predictions about his return to the field or if there even would be such a return. "There was no protocol," Manning recalls, leaving the onus on him and his medical team to build a recovery program from scratch. In July, after his surgeries, Manning flew home to New Orleans to spend time with his parents and his brothers and to align himself mentally for rehab. As he threw around a football with his younger brother Eli, who was also a superstar quarterback for the New York Giants, Peyton struggled to catch passes. After they had played catch for a while, Eli told Peyton, "It looks like you can't finish the throw and get anything on it." As someone who had not missed a football start due to injury since the age of 15, Manning initially had trouble accepting his current state, but he had come to appreciate his career up to that point. Manning looked back fondly on his years on the field, saying, "I'd had this string of good health and good fortune. Good protection, good coaches, good linemen, played in a good system. When you play for 20 years, and really, I never had to miss a game due to injury, that's not just good protection. That's good luck." Even though it had appeared that Manning's good luck had run out, he remembered thinking, "Wow, I got almost 20 years out of this neck. Boy, I'm grateful for the time I've had."[166] Having put his career in perspective after spending time with

---

166 Ibid

his family, especially Cooper, who never got to enjoy a true football career, Manning was mentally ready to begin rehabbing, and he did so with all the meticulousness and determination of a Super Bowl champion and MVP.

Manning traveled to Europe four times to listen to other medical opinions, which according to Manning, "had a little voodoo to them." After the solutions proposed by the European doctors were mostly unsuccessful, Manning shifted his focus to the weight room, where he spent week after week training with five-pound dumbbells in an effort to stimulate reactivation of the nerves in his throwing arm. At this stage in the recovery process, Manning likened throwing a football to "stepping on the gas and there is no gas in the car." "There was nothing I could do about it," Manning recalls. "It was just a real test of patience unlike anything I had to go through." More concerning than this persistent arm weakness was Manning's loss of proprioceptive ability in his arm. Manning explained, "I kind of lost awareness of my arm in space. When you had the same throwing motion for so long — golfers talk about repeating their swing, well, quarterbacks repeat too. But I couldn't repeat. That was scary. Just discouraging." As Manning continued to work on his arm strength and throwing ability, he recalled that the hardest part of the uphill climb was the mental aspect of it. He recalled, "You talk about being pretty disappointed around two in the afternoon when you realize today is not the day."[167] As Manning continued to rehab, everything that could go wrong did go wrong. Manning re-herniated the disc in his neck. For any reasonable person, retirement would seem like the only remaining option. But reasonable people don't tend to be in the "greatest player of all time" conversation either.

After already enduring three surgeries, Manning opted for a more invasive surgical intervention that posed greater risks but potentially offered a more permanent solution. Spine specialist Dr. Robert Watkins conducted a single-level anterior fusion on the vertebrae in question. This procedure involved removing the compromised disc from Manning's spinal cord and then welding his spinal cord together with screws and a metal plate after filling it with a bone graft. The weakness Manning felt after his previous surgeries paled in comparison to the effects of this surgery. In fact, Manning did not even pick up a football until three months after the surgery. A peculiar part of his recovery process was playing darts, and Manning recalls, "I could barely get the thing to stick" when he first threw a dart after the procedure. As Manning welcomed twins with his wife that year, he realized "The one year the Lord took my greatest physical gift, he gave

---

167 Jenkins, Sally. "Peyton Manning on his neck surgeries rehab — and how he almost didn't make it back." The Washington Post. Last modified October 21, 2013. Accessed May 31, 2019. https://www.washingtonpost.com/sports/redskins/peyton-manning-on-his-neck-surgeries-rehab--and-how-he-almost-didnt-make-it-back/

me the greatest gift you could have in children. So that was a real equalizer. And I would take that trade any day of the week." While his main focus was now being a father to his children, Manning was still hell-bent on getting back on the football field.

In December 2011, mere months after his seemingly unending surgical schedule, Manning went to Duke University to work with head coach David Cutcliffe, who was the offensive coordinator at Tennessee during Manning's run with the Vols. According to Manning, "We started at ground zero. It was good going to someone who knew you from the beginning." Manning no longer felt pain thanks to the surgery performed by Dr. Watkins, and each day, Cutcliffe measured Manning's velocity and arm speed and filmed his throws. Although the improvements in Manning's ability were gradual at first, after relentless perseverance, Manning started to look like himself. Cutcliffe recalls, "when he could get the ball into his arm slot, and felt it, God, that was fun to see."[168]

Dr. Watkins finally cleared Manning for an NFL return in February 2012. Although Manning still had weak triceps, his re-injury risk was finally no greater than that of the average

---

168 Jenkins, Sally. "Peyton Manning on his neck surgeries rehab — and how he almost didn't make it back." The Washington Post. Last modified October 21, 2013. Accessed May 31, 2019. https://www.washingtonpost.com/sports/redskins/peyton-manning-on-his-neck-surgeries-rehab--and-how-he-almost-didnt-make-it-back/

player on the field. Watkins advised Manning, "It's your job to learn to compensate for that. The key would be to get [your] legs, core, and other arm sections as strong as possible." Manning credits Watkins for giving him further confidence in his ability to make a return to the NFL, reflecting, "What he kind of said was, 'I think you can still be a thrower with a weak triceps, but everything else needs to fire pretty good.'"[169] As Manning was ready to make his comeback, in March 2012, the Indianapolis Colts released him. As he failed to hold back tears, Manning announced, ""Nobody loves their job more than I do. Nobody loves playing quarterback more than I do. I still want to play. But there is no other team I wanted to play for."[170] As Manning accepted the reality of playing for an NFL team other than the Colts for the first time in his life, he began scheduling private workouts with franchises such as the Broncos, 49ers, and Titans. Reflecting on the process, Manning said, "I wanted them to see me in person. All of them felt my muscles. You could see the atrophy in my arm and right pectoral. I wanted to put it all out on table, and have them say, 'Here's what we think,' rather than show them a video of me. I wanted them to tell me, 'Hey you look good enough to play for us.'" And by the end of the month, the

---

169 Ibid

170 Nathan, Alec. "Peyton Manning Informs Broncos He Will Retire." Bleacher Report. Last modified March 6, 2016. Accessed May 31, 2019. https://bleacherreport.com/articles/2568778-peyton-manning-re-portedly-will-announce-retirement.

Broncos thought Manning looked good enough and signed him to a five-year, $96 million deal.[171]

As the Broncos gave Manning a shot at a comeback, he took the NFL by storm. In 2013, Peyton Manning had the greatest season for a quarterback in history on his way to an NFL-record fifth MVP award. Manning threw for 5,477 yards and 55 touchdowns, both of which still stand as all-time single season records.[172] While Manning already had a first-ballot hall-of-fame career in his time in Indianapolis, his recovery from a debilitating neck injury to come back and shatter nearly every record in the books on the way to a second Super Bowl win in 2016 elevated him into a whole different stratosphere and the GOAT conversation. Upon retiring, Manning held countless NFL records, such as most career passing yards, career touchdowns, comeback wins, and game-winning drives. Even more remarkably, Manning's play has proven to be one of the only things capable of making my dad sit back down after he gets up from that red chair he loves so much.

---

171 Jenkins, Sally. "Peyton Manning on his neck surgeries rehab — and how he almost didn't make it back." The Washington Post. Last modified October 21, 2013. Accessed May 31, 2019. https://www.washingtonpost.com/sports/redskins/peyton-manning-on-his-neck-surgeries-rehab--and-how-he-almost-didnt-make-it-back/

172 Dator, James. "Here's a list of every major NFL record Peyton Manning holds." SB Nation. Last modified March 6, 2016. Accessed May 31, 2019. https://www.sbnation.com/nfl/2014/10/19/7010081/peyton-manning-nfl-record-list-most-touchdowns-509.

CHAPTER 10

DREW BREES: THE SIGNATURE PATIENT

———

December 31, 2005. In the waning minutes of the first half of a game against the Denver Broncos, Drew Brees played his last snap as a San Diego Charger. As Brees wound back his right arm to throw a pass from his own end zone, he was stripped by free safety John Lynch. Brees dropped the ball, which quickly wobbled up the field, and the defense broke loose, chasing the football with reckless abandon. Brees rushed to the ball and slid in the grass in an effort to clean up his own mess, 325-pound defensive tackle Gerard Warren dove on top of him. Warren quickly rolled off of Brees, who slowly contorted to his side before awkwardly making his way to his feet.[173]

"As crazy as it sounds, I knew exactly what my injury was when I got up off the ground," the Pro Bowl quarterback recalls. "I could feel that basically, my shoulder was out of place. It was a dislocated right throwing shoulder. I mean, if you could rank the worst injuries that you could have as a quarterback, that is right up there."[174]

As legendary Chargers running back LaDainian Tomlinson looked back on the infamous moment, he recalled, "The initial play, I was in disbelief. Like, I just didn't believe he was hurt that bad. We were very close, and we worked out together. And so, to see him holding his shoulder, I was just was thinking like 'oh, you know it's just a bad sprain, it's not that bad, it'll be ok.'"[175]

Brees' wife, Brittany Brees, recalled with tears in her eyes, "We were in a suite with his friends and our family and, you

173 "'9 for No. 9: A Champion's Journey' | Drew Brees | Ch 4: The Injury." Video file. YouTube. Posted by New Orleans Saints, September 4, 2018. Accessed May 31, 2019. https://www.youtube.com/watch?v=_79b2HUu9js.

174 Ibid

175 Ibid

know, he went down, and I just knew that was it. We were gone. He walked off the field with his arm just locked up."[176]

In Birmingham, Alabama, Dr. James Andrews could not believe what he had just seen on his TV screen. "I happened to be watching the game on TV, and I saw him get hurt. They showed it again on replay, and I could tell that he was diving for a ball down on his goal line, then some lineman fell across his body and made his arm go way over his head and he walked out with his right shoulder caught as he came off the sideline. Having been there, watching that in slow motion and watching him walk off, I knew that he had knocked his Humeral head out of the socket inferiorly, which is down at the bottom, which is really unusual. It's called a subluxation erecta, and it is locked there at the bottom of the socket. I said, 'oh my goodness, he's dislocated his shoulder at the bottom.'"[177]

Almost instantly as he began to gingerly walk off of the field, Brees understood the gravity of what he had just endured. He remembers, "I thought to myself, 'You know, this is probably the last time that I ever put on a Charger uniform. And then reality really sinks in and I say, 'this might be the last time I put on a football uniform.' As I'm walking off, my whole body is just numb. It was just numb with shock. It wasn't really so

---

176 Ibid
177 Ibid

much the pain, it was just knowing the reality of what this was." As he came to terms with the critical injury he had sustained, Brees began looking forward. "I just took a deep breath and said, 'one day at a time,' and let's see how serious this is."[178]

Two days after suffering what had then appeared to be a career-threatening injury, Brees and his camp reached out to Dr. James Andrews and agreed to meet him in Birmingham so he could evaluate Brees. According to Brees, "It takes a few days. I quit feeling sorry for myself."[179]

"Dr. Andrews was known to be the guy to go to," Brittany Brees recalls. Drew Brees looked back fondly on his initial meeting with Dr. Andrews, smiling as he said, "I remember him looking at me and saying, 'basically, I've never quite seen anything like this. I know that it is serious. I know I can fix it. I just don't know exactly what I need to do quite yet because I think once I get in there, I might find out some more.' I feel like I'm in good hands, right?"[180]

According to Dr. Andrews, "the MRI indicated that he was pretty torn up with his labrum and cuff. You look down at

178 "'9 for No. 9: A Champion's Journey' | Drew Brees | Ch 4: The Injury." Video file. YouTube. Posted by New Orleans Saints, September 4, 2018. Accessed May 31, 2019. https://www.youtube.com/watch?v=_79b2HUu9js.

179 Ibid

180 Ibid

the bottom of his shoulder, his arm went from being in this [normal] position and went up, up, up, and over. In a super overhead position. And when it did, the arm bone went out the bottom. Which is really unusual. [Brees'] main deal was that he wanted to know [if] I had to cut to fix it or could I do it arthroscopically. I think he was worried if I had to cut, make an incision, that he knew that was a harder thing to come back from and he was, of course, worried about his career." At the time, Brees knew he had torn his labrum, but he did not know how severely his rotator cuff was damaged. In fact, the odds of suffering the injury Brees had suffered were 1-in-500. "So when I went under," Brees recalls, "I really didn't know what the extent of that surgery was going to be."[181]

As Brees was placed under anesthesia and an arthroscope (a medical tool used to open up joints) was placed into his shoulder, Dr. Andrews said, "We were able to truly identify all of the pathology. He had a 360-degree labrum tear all the way around his shoulder, particularly involving the bottom of his shoulder, where the labrum attaches to the socket. The thing we were a little bit surprised with was that he had a complete tear of the undersurface of his supraspinatus and infraspinatus — his rotator cuff — and we had to repair all of that. It was an extensive procedure, and if you couldn't do it as a team and get it done quickly, your shoulder would be

_____

181 Ibid

like a watermelon with swelling and you wouldn't be able to complete the procedure."[182]

As the anesthesia wore off and Brees awoke, he turned to the nurse and immediately asked, "Did he have to cut?" As the nurse looked at Brees' chart and suggested the surgery looked like it had required the team of doctors to cut, Dr. Andrews walked in and informed Brees that despite requiring 11 anchors in his labrum and two anchors in his rotator cuff, Brees' injury was repaired arthroscopically and did not require the doctors to cut. Brees recalls, "I'm still coming out of it and I'm down and he puts his hand on my shoulder and in true Dr. Andrews fashion, he said 'if I did that surgery a hundred times, I couldn't do it as good as I did it this time.' And I kind of perked up and I was like, 'really?' From a man like that with a reputation like that to say [that], it helped me breathe a sigh of relief. He said, 'you got 13 anchors in there — 11 in your labrum and two in your rotator cuff." According to Dr. Andrews, "I wanted to plant that positive seed in his mind so that he knew that he could get well. It made it a lot better prognosis to be able to put all that back arthroscopically because it was less trauma and less injury by surgery to the shoulder joint."[183]

---

182 Ibid

183 "'9 for No. 9: A Champion's Journey' | Drew Brees | Ch 4: The Injury." Video file. YouTube. Posted by New Orleans Saints, September 4, 2018. Accessed May 31, 2019. https://www.youtube.com/watch?v=_79b2HUu9js.

Coming back from a major injury was something Drew Brees had experience with. In the December of his junior year at Austin Westlake High School, Brees tore his ACL. As a long recovery process loomed in front of him at the time, Brees assured doctors that he would be back for not only his senior season of football, but also for the summer baseball season. Furthermore, this particular recovery, which lasted around six months, was beneficial for Brees in terms of improving his strength as a whole. According to Brees, "at the time, I was 6-foot, 170 pounds. By the end of that six-month rehabilitation process, I was 6-foot, 195 pounds."[184] Using the same headstrong attitude he used to exceed doctors' expectations as a high school quarterback recovering from a major knee injury, Brees began to attack his shoulder rehab with a competitive ferocity.

With his surgery successfully completed, Brees' focus now shifted to the lengthy rehabilitation process lying in front of him. According to Brees, "Then I knew, okay, it's all about the rehab and said, 'all right, what's the rehab looking like.' Eight months. Eight months. You know, that's a daunting thing to think about. As much as I wanted to believe in my heart that I was going to come back and I was going to come

---

184 Erickson, Joel A. "The story of Drew Brees and the '1-in-500 injury' that couldn't stop his historic career." The New Orleans Advocate. Last modified October 7, 2018. Accessed May 31, 2019. https://www. theadvocate.com/new_orleans/sports/saints/article_abaf4c0a-c805-11e8-9412-2391641ec153.html.

back stronger and that was my mindset and everything in my being was saying that, still, there was reality, I hope I can come back and do this." Then-teammate LaDainian Tomlinson was positive that Brees had what it took to recover from such a drastic injury, saying, "Even when news came down about how serious the injury was, I knew with his work ethic that Drew would bounce back."[185]

In order to take on the seemingly impossible task of getting his shoulder back into NFL form, Brees moved to Birmingham for over four months in order to work with Dr. Kevin Wilk. According to Dr. Andrews, "the thing that really got him to a high level of being able to throw a football and be able to be in the Super Bowl is the work that he and Kevin Wilk did in rehabilitation. They were like Siamese twins for about four, five, or six months." Dr. Wilk initially told Brees that although he could likely get back to throwing in eight months, it could take Brees up to two years to start feeling like his old self. According to Brees, "That's overwhelming to hear, that type of prognosis. So I said, 'let's not look too far out, let's set short-term goals. When can I get out of this sling?' And he said, 'Well, that's four weeks,' and I said, 'I'm going to beat that.'" And in three weeks, after hours upon

---

185 "'9 for No. 9: A Champion's Journey' | Drew Brees | Ch 4: The Injury." Video file. YouTube. Posted by New Orleans Saints, September 4, 2018. Accessed May 31, 2019. https://www.youtube.com/watch?v=_79b2HUu9js.

hours of work on strengthening his shoulder, Brees had his right arm out of a sling.[186]

Dr. Wilk continued to prove to be a crucial part of Brees' rehab process. Brees looks back on his time working with Dr. Wilk as a defining moment of his career, explaining, "it took me from being at one level to a whole other level."[187] After Brees strengthened his shoulder to the point where he no longer needed to wear a sling, the next goal was to regain a full range of motion. Dr. Wilk told Brees that this process would take nine weeks; however, Brees managed to complete this part of the rehab process in just six weeks. Brees fondly recalls, "Whatever they told me, I said I was gonna beat that, and they'd get mad at me, tell me, 'it's got to heal,' and I said we can beat it."[188]

After he had fully recovered, Brees recalls feeling like he was starting over in terms of throwing a football. "In regards to

186 Erickson, Joel A. "The story of Drew Brees and the '1-in-500 injury' that couldn't stop his historic career." The New Orleans Advocate. Last modified October 7, 2018. Accessed May 31, 2019. https://www. theadvocate.com/new_orleans/sports/saints/article_abaf4c0a-c805-11e8-9412-2391641ec153.html.

187 Drew Brees My Professional Care Story." Video file. YouTube. Posted by PerformanceHealth, August 30, 2017. Accessed May 31, 2019. https://www.youtube.com/watch?v=4ChGRy9TXWw.

188 Erickson, Joel A. "The story of Drew Brees and the '1-in-500 injury' that couldn't stop his historic career." The New Orleans Advocate. Last modified October 7, 2018. Accessed May 31, 2019. https://www. theadvocate.com/new_orleans/sports/saints/article_abaf4c0a-c805-11e8-9412-2391641ec153.html.

the way I was now developing the muscular structure and strength around my shoulder, I felt like not only was I going to come back and throw the ball as well, but I was going to throw it better. And I was also equipped with a protocol that would allow me to become stronger and stronger throwing the football and then also sustain longer." A major part of the protocol Brees followed to strengthen his shoulder is the Theraband CLX, a training band that incorporates functions from a variety of strength-building equipment, such as loops, bands, tubes with handles, and door anchors. According to Brees, "I use the Theraband CLX both in my active warmup and also on the back end after I throw as just part of my maintenance program. I trust so much of the protocols that Kevin has put together for me over the years... Especially, Theraband CLX exercises not only get me back to healthy, but also where I feel like at the end of the day, I'm even stronger than when I walked in the door."[189]

As the once Pro Bowl-caliber Drew Brees took the field for the New Orleans Saints as the team's starting quarterback at the start of the 2006 NFL season, a cloud of uncertainty surrounded not only Brees and the Saints, but the entire city of New Orleans. In August 2005, Hurricane Katrina struck the northern coast of the Gulf of Mexico, devastating Louisiana

---

189 "Drew Brees My Professional Care Story." Video file. YouTube. Posted by PerformanceHealth, August 30, 2017. Accessed May 31, 2019. https://www.youtube.com/watch?v=4ChGRy9TXWw.

and the city of New Orleans. The devastating tropical storm resulted in 1,833 recorded deaths, an estimated $125 billion in damage, and countless lives forever changed due to property damage — a majority of which was endured by New Orleans and Louisiana.[190] As the city focused on rebuilding itself in 2006, the task of rebuilding the Saints was placed squarely on the surgically repaired shoulder of Drew Brees.

Brees was at the helm of an undermanned Saints team that went 3-13 in the 2005 season prior to Brees' arrival. Brees' takeover at quarterback carried with it the hopes of a city that desperately needed something to look forward to. Defying all odds, Brees threw for over 4,400 yards while racking up 26 passing touchdowns as he started every single game for the Saints that season.[191] Brees made the Miami Dolphins look foolish for passing on him in the previous offseason to sign the mediocre quarterback Daunte Culpepper instead. Furthermore, with Sean Payton's elite coaching and game plan centered around Brees, the Saints went 10-6, improving by seven games from the previous season and making it all the way to the NFC Championship game.

---

190 CNN Library. "Hurricane Katrina Statistics Fast Facts." CNN. Last modified August 30, 2018. Accessed May 31, 2019. https://www.cnn.com/2013/08/23/us/hurricane-katrina-statistics-fast-facts/index.html.

191 "2006 New Orleans Saints Statistics & Players." Pro Football Reference. Last modified 2019. Accessed May 31, 2019. https://www.pro-football-reference.com/teams/nor/2006.htm.

In the following seasons, Brees set the league on fire. Although the Saints did not make the playoffs again until the 2009 season, in the two seasons following their 2006 breakthrough, Drew Brees showed that he was not only a Pro Bowl quarterback but a Hall-of-Famer. In 2007, Brees passed for 4,423 yards and 28 touchdowns, a campaign he followed up on in 2008 with a whopping 5,069 passing yards and 34 touchdowns.[192] [193] Brees continued his excellent play into the 2009 season – a season in which his 4,388 yards and 34 touchdowns in just 15 games propelled the Saints to a 13-3 record and a playoff berth.[194]

As the Saints geared up for the 2009 playoffs, the first postseason they had qualified for since Brees' inaugural 2006 season, New Orleans came together as a city of fans. In the past three years, they had witnessed the ups and downs of the Saints putting together the correct pieces to win with a generationally talented quarterback holding the reins. They had also persevered through the tragedy of Hurricane Katrina, showing that and although the storm has resulted in innumerable

---

192 "2007 New Orleans Saints Statistics & Players." Pro Football Reference. Last modified 2019. Accessed May 31, 2019. https://www.pro-football-reference.com/teams/nor/2007.htm.

193 "2008 New Orleans Saints Statistics & Players." Pro Football Reference. Last modified 2019. Accessed May 31, 2019. https://www.pro-football-reference.com/teams/nor/2008.htm.

194 "2009 New Orleans Saints Statistics & Players." Pro Football Reference. Last modified 2019. Accessed May 31, 2019. https://www.pro-football-reference.com/teams/nor/2009.htm.

losses and utter devastation, it had also brought out displays of humanity and compassion between New Orleanians.

With a city united behind him, Brees led the Saints into battle. In the divisional round of the playoffs, the Saints made easy work of the Arizona Cardinals as they cruised to a 45-14 victory behind Brees' 247 yards and 3 touchdowns.[195] The Saints won a nail-biter the following week in the NFC Championship against the Minnesota Vikings with Brees leading the way, racking up 197 yards and 3 touchdowns in a 31-28 overtime win against gunslinger Brett Favre.[196] With a Super Bowl matchup set against Peyton Manning and the Indianapolis Colts in Dolphin Stadium, the very stadium home to the team that passed on Brees in 2006, all eyes were trained on the impending heavyweight bout between Manning and Brees, two of the most dominant quarterbacks of the millennium.

As a little under six minutes remained in the fourth quarter of Super Bowl XLIV, the Saints found themselves down to the Colts, 16-17. As the Saints offense lined up at the Colts' 2-yard

195 "Divisional Round - Arizona Cardinals at New Orleans Saints - January 16th, 2010." Pro Football Reference. Last modified 2019. Accessed May 31, 2019. https://www.pro-football-reference.com/boxscores/201001160nor.htm.

196 "NFC Championship - Minnesota Vikings at New Orleans Saints - January 24th, 2010." Pro Football Reference. Last modified 2019. Accessed May 31, 2019. https://www.pro-football-reference.com/boxscores/201001240nor.htm.

line, Brees barked orders to his offensive line as he began to squat under the center, positioning his hands to take the snap. As Brees took the snap, he quickly took a single step back and rotated his body to the right, firing a dart to the cutting tight-end Jeremy Shockey. Shockey was instantly wrapped up by a Colts defender and fell on his back. As he arose, clutching the football in one hand, the crowd erupted into a frenzy. Touchdown. As the Saints defense eventually took care of business, sealing the game on a 74-yard interception return for a touchdown by Tracy Porter, the Saints sideline broke out into celebration, dumping Gatorade on head coach Sean Payton, whose face was filled with boyish joy.[197]

Brees was the obvious choice for Super Bowl MVP, earning the illustrious honor with 288 passing yards to go with 2 big touchdowns and 0 interceptions.[198] As Brees hoisted up the shimmering Vince Lombardi trophy and kissed it, it was clear he had completed his comeback to NFL superstardom. As Brees helped the Saints bring home their first Super Bowl title in franchise history, he cemented his place in the annals of New Orleans history while giving New Orleanians

---

197 "Super Bowl XLIV: Saints vs. Colts highlights." Video file. YouTube. Posted by NFL, February 6, 2015. Accessed May 31, 2019. https://www.youtube.com/watch?v=PozuCOfcSjc.

198 "Super Bowl XLIV - New Orleans Saints vs. Indianapolis Colts - February 7th, 2010." Pro Football Reference. Last modified 2019. Accessed May 31, 2019. https://www.pro-football-reference.com/boxscores/201002070clt.htm.

renewed hope that they could get through any roadblock placed in their way, no matter how monumental.

A surprise to many around the NFL, Brees' incredible recovery came as no shock to two of the people who believed in his abilities the most: Dr. James Andrews and Brees himself. According to Dr. Andrews, "I have what I call 'signature patients' that really changed my career, and I changed their careers. And I would say that the number one signature patient in that category was Drew Brees with his shoulder injury, which was around 12 years ago or so, and he is still playing, and he is still breaking records. The injury that he had to his shoulder was one that was an unbelievable result to get him well. But you have to realize, we have another saying in sports medicine: if you pick the right patient to operate on, he can make you look pretty good as a physician and as a surgeon. And Drew Brees' work ethic and motivation are the reason he got well. So, to think about him and what he went through and what he did and how hard he worked is unbelievable, and it makes me look good, but really it wasn't me, it was him."

As Drew Brees continued to lead the Saints to win after win in the 2018 season as a possible favorite to win the regular-season MVP award, over a decade after suffering an injury many vowed was career-ending, the whole process has become a blur for him. According to Brees, "Before I knew it, I was throwing a football again, signed with the New Orleans Saints, and here we are, almost 13 years later, and I'm still going strong."[199] Dr. Andrews asserts that the Saints could not have made a decision better than giving Brees a second chance at professional football, reiterating, "He's probably one in a hundred that could come back from that injury at a high level. But he was the right one. And I believe in him for one more go. The New Orleans Saints believed in him and they signed him, and you've seen what he's done for the Saints."[200]

A day after watching Drew Brees throw a 62-yard touchdown pass that broke Peyton Manning's NFL record for career passing yards, Dr. James Andrews was ecstatic. "Seeing somebody like Drew Brees break the passing record the other night, I slept great that night because I was so proud of him. In those categories, you don't think about it as you being the reason that he is successful. Most of those guys are super successful like that because of who they are, the fact that they are good athletes to being with, and because they work so hard and they are motivated. So the credit all goes back to them. You don't take credit for anything like that, and

199 Erickson, Joel A. "The story of Drew Brees and the '1-in-500 injury' that couldn't stop his historic career." The New Orleans Advocate. Last modified October 7, 2018. Accessed May 31, 2019. https://www. theadvocate.com/new_orleans/sports/saints/article_abaf4c0a-c805-11e8-9412-2391641ec153.html.

200 "drew brees injury + rehab." Video file. YouTube. Posted by Robert Sevier, December 9, 2010. Accessed May 31, 2019. https://www.youtube.com/watch?v=io5pOS8WPIo.

if you are looking for credit, you're not really going to be that good of a doctor. It's an enjoyment, and I call that the joy of sports medicine. Certainly, losing is no fun."

From wondering if he had thrown his last passing yards to having thrown more passing yards than anyone who has ever put on an NFL jersey, Drew Brees is the quintessential example of what is possible when sports intersect with medicine. According to Brees, "At the time when I tore my ACL in high school or when I dislocated my shoulder, at those moments, I thought that was the worst thing that could ever happen to me. I now look back at those moments and say, those were probably two of the best things that could have ever happened to me."[201] Without the help of physicians like Dr. James Andrews, Drew Brees' renaissance as the New Orleans Saints' quarterback would have been an impossibility.

As Brees puts it, "I owe that man my career."[202]

---

201 Erickson, Joel A. "The story of Drew Brees and the '1-in-500 injury' that couldn't stop his historic career." The New Orleans Advocate. Last modified October 7, 2018. Accessed May 31, 2019. https://www.theadvocate.com/new_orleans/sports/saints/article_abaf4c0a-c805-11e8-9412-2391641ec153.html.

202 Ibid

CHAPTER 11

GIANCARLO STANTON: JUST A FEW MISSING TEETH

The numbers spoke for themselves: 59 home runs. 20 more than the closest National League player and more than anyone in the last 16 years. 132 RBIs, more than anyone in baseball. 91 extra-base hits, more than anyone else in baseball. A 0.631 slugging percentage. You guessed it: more than anyone else in baseball. But Giancarlo Stanton's 2017 National League MVP award was surprising for many reasons. Sure, the Marlins were a terrible team who were nowhere close to making the playoffs. Sure, Joey Votto had an on-base percentage that was on another level. Yeah, Paul Goldschmidt was the only NL MVP candidate who was on a team that qualified for the playoffs.[203] But most of all, it was shocking that Stanton was playing at this level in the first place. Or maybe that he was playing at all.

A little over three years before he was declared the National League's MVP, Giancarlo Stanton was on pace to lead the National League in home runs and take home the coveted MVP award. That was, until he was writhing in the dirt of the batter's box in Milwaukee after taking an 88-mile-per-hour fastball to his face. As the pitch was launched into Stanton's face, the announcers exclaimed "oh my gosh!" as pitcher Mike Fiers immediately threw his hands on his head in horror.[204] As the medical staff sprinted to the side of the 6'6" 250-pound superstar, the entire ballpark fell silent – in awe of seeing someone so massive look so helpless. As Stanton was stretchered off the field to be rushed to the hospital, baseball fans around the world wondered if that was the last time they would see the slugger pick up a bat.

Stanton had suffered an orbital bone fracture, and his face had been bloodied and swollen to look like there was a lemon

203 Spencer, Clark. "Here's why the Marlins' Giancarlo Stanton may win the MVP — and why he may not." Miami Herald. Last modified nov 16, 2017. Accessed May 31, 2019. https://www.miamiherald.com/sports/spt-columns-blogs/fish-bytes/article184964153.html.

204 "Giancarlo Stanton Hit in the Face with Pitch - FULL VIDEO." Video file. YouTube. Posted by G4MarchMadnessHD, September 11, 2014. Accessed May 31, 2019. https://www.youtube.com/watch?v=sBQPk9Bva14.

on the side of his face. According to oculo-plastic surgeon Dr. John Martin, Stanton was fortunate to still have his vision, as "the orbital bone is there to protect the eye, but with a ball going 88 mph, it could have crushed the bones completely and you could lose your vision completely or lose your eye completely."[205] After receiving further treatment and undergoing dental surgeries, Stanton was optimistic about his situation. "I could have my mouth wired shut now," he explained. "I could have a plate in my face. I could have a lot of things. I'll take a few missing teeth over all that."[206] Stanton was set to begin his comeback to baseball. "You hear about people losing their eye, or you lose vision," he elucidated, confidently saying, "As long as I'm able to see, that's the big career thing."[207]

205 Spencer, Clark, and Manny NavarroMiami Marlins' Giancarlo Stanton suffers facial fractures, likely won't return this season By Clark Spencer and Manny Navarro Read more here: https://www.miamiherald.com/sports/mlb/miami-marlins/article2087465.html#storylink=cpy. "Miami Marlins' Giancarlo Stanton suffers facial fractures, likely won't return this season." Miami Herald. Last modified September 12, 2014. Accessed May 31, 2019. https://www.miamiherald.com/sports/mlb/miami-marlins/article2087465.html.

206 Associated Press. "Giancarlo Stanton: Could be worse." ESPN. Last modified September 19, 2014. Accessed May 31, 2019. http://www.espn.com/mlb/story/_/id/11549652/giancarlo-stanton-miami-marlins-says-recovering-well-facial-injuries.

207 Frisaro, Joe. "Stanton upbeat, thankful hit to face wasn't worse." MLB.com. Last modified September 18, 2014. Accessed May 31, 2019. https://www.mlb.com/news/marlins-giancarlo-stanton-upbeat-thankful-hit-to-face-wasnt-worse/c-95316098.

Although Stanton was confident in his physical abilities, he was less sanguine about the mental hurdle that would accompany stepping back into the batter's box. Stanton lamented, "But to be back into the box, and in competition, I'm not quite sure. I think when we decide the protection that will be on, I'll have more reassurance wearing that. I don't know."[208]

But as he made his way back to the baseball field, the only thing that had changed about Stanton was his helmet. As he cranked home run after home run wearing a new helmet with a flap covering his jaw, it was clear that Stanton was back and as good as he ever was. "I knew I had to bounce back from that," Stanton declares, crediting the medical professionals around him, explaining "it was really people pushing me, my trainers, the people I work out with and try to get better with, they always pushed me, they always said, 'You can do this, you can be there.' And I knew I can do it, but I knew that it took more than talking about it. You had to show up every day, be prepared and do everything you need to."[209] With the help of the Marlins' medical staff, Stanton had stormed back onto the scene, capturing the elusive MVP award that had nearly evaded him three years earlier. Stanton said "It was tough physically recovering, but it wasn't tough to get

208 Ibid
209 Frisaro, Joe. "Stanton fishes out close vote, wins NL MVP." MLB.com. Last modified November 16, 2017. Accessed May 31, 2019. https://www.mlb.com/news/marlins-giancarlo-stanton-wins-nl-mvp-award-c262051396.

back in the box" thanks to the help of his medical team.[210] As the newly crowned MVP was traded to the New York Yankees, a team that boasts a winning pedigree suitable for a player of Giancarlo Stanton's caliber, he continued to rake moonshot after moonshot. For the first time, he was playing for a franchise that was contending for the World Series. And there's nothing like living in New York or watching baseball with my dad when the Yankees are winning.

210 Martin, Dan. "The only thing that remains from Giancarlo Stanton's moment of terror." New York Post. Last modified March 11, 2018. Accessed May 31, 2019. https://nypost.com/2018/03/11/the-only-thing-that-remains-from-giancarlo-stantons-moment-of-terror/.

CHAPTER 12

IVAN TCHATCHOUWO: MORE THAN AN ATHLETE

As Ivan Tchatchouwo sat in the Concordia College locker room, he took it all in. The journey here had been anything but ordinary. For the first time in a long time, he stopped and looked back at it, and he was content. Having captained Concordia College to its first-ever CACC conference tournament berth was something he could never have dreamt of as a wide-eyed 7-year-old moving to the Bronx from Cameroon. When his family first moved to New York, Tchatchouwo would go to the soccer field after school, eager to make new friends, but leave unsuccessful after no one would else would show up. The vast yet empty soccer fields of the Bronx differed starkly from the fields

Tchatchouwo was used to in Cameroon, which were modest, yet replete with hundreds of children eager to play for hours on end after school, regardless of whether they had the proper shoes.

Determined to make new friends and realizing that soccer was not going to be the way for him to do so, Ivan decided to try his luck at the basketball courts instead. He was no natural, and the other kids laughed as they watched the kid with the baggy clothes brick shots off of the backboard one after the other. Eventually, however, these bricks turned into swishes, and Ivan grew to 6'3" with a taste in fashion that was just as large. He was a standout guard at All Hallows' High School, and he eventually secured a scholarship to play at Concordia College despite quitting the team his senior year.

The adjustment to the college game was a tough one for Tchatchouwo, and while he struggled on the court, he was stressed off of it. The coach who recruited him got fired after his freshman year. He was worried about his scholarship. He was unsure if he would still be able to play on the team or even attend Concordia College. Ivan pushed through, and his sophomore year was one marked by improvements all around. But he was not satisfied, and he was willing to do whatever it took to become great. The summer after his sophomore year, Ivan sacrificed everything. "It was workout, basketball, sleep. Workout, basketball, sleep. Workout, basketball, sleep," he recalls. Until he tore his meniscus. One day, he was doing routine sprints by himself on the track. "I was mid-sprint and I just collapsed," Tchatchouwo recalls. To this day, he remembers, "I had to crawl to my phone and call my teammates in agony. Then I found out when I got to campus it was over. All from a routine track session." As he sat on the table, the team doctor told him that would likely need arthroscopic surgery to repair the ligament. Ivan could no longer contribute on the court, and he suffered off of it. His grades dropped. His self-worth dropped. He was terrified. "I was depressed," he remembers vividly, "I was scared no one would like me if I wasn't out on that court." But that was before he met Dr. Guy Voyer.

As he sat with Dr. Voyer, Ivan felt something new. He had been in this position before: sitting in a doctor's office, getting his knee looked at. He had felt the soreness in his knee before, right where his meniscus had torn, wondering if all the work he put in over the summer had been in vain. Something just didn't feel quite right. But as he sat and watched Voyer stretch his knee, easily conversing with him in French, the language he grew up speaking in Cameroon, for the first time in a long time, Ivan felt relief. "I felt tugs in tissues I didn't even realize I had," he recalls. "I remember thinking, 'I should be fine.'" The pain was still there, but he felt good. Dr. Voyer told him he would not need surgery and reassured him that together, they would strengthen the muscles and ligaments in and around his knee to make up for the tear in his meniscus. Dr. Voyer was confident that Ivan's injury was not as bad as it seemed, and if he made his knee stronger, he would not need surgery to repair the meniscus. That was music to Ivan's ears. As he continued to do his rehab exercises and push himself to return to the sport that had come to mean everything, Ivan was molding himself into an even better player, one that was focused on injury prevention and putting the best version of himself out there on the court each and every night. "Sports gave me the tools I needed to find myself and succeed," he happily declared as he thinks back to his time as a student-athlete. The role of physicians in bringing about that reality? "So pivotal and crucial," Ivan says, without a doubt in his mind.

Ivan also saw a sports psychologist. "I started opening up," he says, pausing for a second. "He helped me realize that I was more than an athlete." Tchatchouwo realized that there was more to life than basketball, even though basketball was something that seemed to consume every waking hour of his days. He began to understand that people would love and appreciate him even if he was spending hours studying for a test instead of spending hours putting up jumpers in the gym. Eventually, he got back in game shape, and just in time. He had been voted a captain by his teammates, and it was time to lead them to battle. As the Concordia College basketball team overcame the myriad of doubts they had faced and went on to have the best basketball season in program history, Tchatchouwo underwent a similar journey of unprecedented success. As he overcame the doubts in his own mind, one thing became clear: He was more than an athlete. He was capable of incredible things, whether that meant taking over late in games or spending hours in the library working toward his biology degree. His doctors had shown him that he was more than an athlete. Basketball taught him life.

Ivan Tchatchouwo is the founder, president, and CEO of The Zone, an organization that aims to empower future generations by teaching them life lessons through basketball. Through a unique focus on biomechanics and data analytics, Tchatchouwo teaches young athletes how to be efficient both on and off the court. "You are investing in your money, career, and future by investing in your bodies," he preaches. As he provides young athletes access to some of the same technology as the pros, from Normatec Machines to advanced jump shot analytics, Tchatchouwo is revolutionizing youth basketball. With a focus on using sports to teach life lessons and mental toughness, he is training not only the next generation of elite basketball players, but the next generation of compassionate humans with a focus that extends beyond their time on the hardwood. Tchatchouwo is also currently pursuing a master's degree from Columbia University in applied physiology and biomechanics. Once a promising student-athlete worried about whether a knee injury would derail his basketball career, a little help from doctors had made it quickly apparent that Ivan Tchatchouwo's involvement with the sport is just getting started.

CHAPTER 13

DREW MUSGRAVE: HOCKEY TO A HOYA

———

On our second day at college, I was preparing to head over to the gym on Georgetown University's campus, affectionately referred to as Yates by Hoyas. As I snugly fit the first pod of my headphones into my left ear, I turned back and asked the roommate who I had no idea I would be spending a vast majority of my time with over the next few years if he played any sports. "Um, sure. In high school, I played hockey, baseball, football, golf, and I ran track." I couldn't help but burst out laughing. Now, I am by no means an elite athlete — I did Taekwondo throughout high school and even won a New York State championship in sparring and form — but here I was, nowhere close to the athlete Drew is, asking him if he played any sports. After about 15 seconds of Drew staring blankly at me, confused, I smiled and replied, "so yes, you play sports."

As Drew accompanied with me to Yates to play pick-up basketball that we would end up playing with an almost religious regularity over the course of the next few years, it was clear that he was an elite athlete. It was no surprise that his first word was not "mom" or "dad," but rather "ball." What was also clear, however, was that he could not hoop at all. The first few times we played basketball, it wasn't even close. Although he played hard and put every ounce of energy into stifling me on defense, Drew couldn't shoot. At all. His shots careened off the top of the backboard. They clanged off the bottom of the rim. They hit the side of the backboard and rolled all the way to the other side of the gym by the treadmills.

Pretty soon, our 1-on-1 games turned into 2-on-2s. Our friends Luc and Shrayus fell in love with the indoor courts of Yates with us. Before long, we had our friends Raghav and Mahesh joining in on the competitiveness as we ran 3-on-3s. Of course, word of our biweekly pick-up basketball games spread, and Vincent and Sud became regulars. We started playing full-court 4-on-4. These basketball games became a way for us to all take a step away from our grueling course loads and all the stress of college. I always joked around with Drew after we left the basketball courts at Yates, beads of sweat dripping off our faces and onto the meticulously glossed hardwood floors. "Bro, once you start hitting your shots and figure out how to play defense, it's game over." And I genuinely believed what I was saying. What I couldn't believe, however, was how fast this would happen. Within two months, Drew was diving after loose balls. Snatching down rebounds. Even occasionally stepping out and hitting a 3-pointer. To this day, anytime we're picking teams and I'm a team captain, I take Drew first overall just so I don't have to deal with him guarding me.

I challenged Drew, and he rose to it. As we continued to face bigger, seemingly impossible challenges, from finding time to continue our pick-up games as we took on new commitments to finding time to sleep while we grinded out tedious organic chemistry lab reports, the two of us continued to push each other forward, promising each other we would get through it. What I did not learn until much later, though, was that these challenges were the least of Drew's worries. The grueling course load that would test our resolve every weekend we spent buried in books while our friends went out and explored Washington, D.C. paled in comparison to the recovery Drew faced after getting a concussion. It paled in comparison to the recovery Drew faced after getting three concussions.

"My first concussion happened in middle school football," Drew recalled. "I had the ball, made it to the edge, got the corner, and then I was forced out of bounds. But there was a late hit that was way far out of bounds and I fell backwards. My head hit a wooden post that was part of the stands, and that was the first concussion I ever had. I was 14. I was very sensitive to light; my head would hurt anytime I would start running and get my blood pumping." As a talented young player with a potential high school career in front of him, Drew would play with extra caution when he returned to the field, trying his best to keep his head upright and avoid helmet contact. Unfortunately, his efforts were in vain.

"My second concussion came in my sophomore year, playing high school varsity football. I played cornerback, the running back was coming around the edge on a sweep. I was always taught to dive at feet because I'm not a really big guy, so there was no way I could have tackled this guy if I tackled him high. So I dove at this dude's feet and got him on the ground, but his knee hit me in the head and I was down and out." Symptoms from concussions tend to worsen after a person suffers more than one of them. The effects of multiple concussions are compounded. For Drew, the previously bothersome direct sunlight became excruciating. Running suddenly became the hardest thing on the planet next to reading.

"At this point, I was starting to think about college and what I wanted to do. My best and favorite sport was hockey, but I was pretty good at football too. I was starting to get looks, and I was going to try to use sports to get into some of the more prestigious schools because I had the academics to get there, but I wanted to increase my chances. After my second concussion, it sounds horrible to say, but I needed to 'save' the remaining concussions for hockey because that was the sport that I had the best chance of getting into a college with."

There wasn't much for Drew to do after this latest concussion, with the only real plan being to ensure he got enough rest while simultaneously bringing his brain power back to where it was prior to his concussions. "This whole time, my parents were watching me very carefully. My dad is an orthopedic surgeon and my mom is a pharmacist, so of course, my treatment was well-regimented and well-adhered to and there was a constant level of care. The training staff did an excellent job and they were a great first step, but they could not provide total care. I got that at home." Whether it was urging him to drink enough water to recognizing that every minute of sleep counted and making him go to sleep early whenever possible, Drew's parents were his backbone throughout his recovery process. He returned to his prior levels of prowess in the classroom and the field, receiving visits from major football powerhouses.

"It was great until my junior year of high school. The day before opening day, we're going through a walk-through. No pads or anything. A pass was coming my way and

I went up for it to knock it down and do my job. And I don't remember much after that. I was told that I had gone head-to-head with the receiver and then after that, had fallen and hit my head again on the ground." Just when things seemed to be going right for Drew, who had prided himself on maintaining a balance between playing a sport each season and being an honor student, the equilibrium he had persevered so diligently to preserve came crashing down around him. "After that, I quit football," Drew recalled, shaking his head. "Every concussion I had ever sustained came from football, and cost-benefit analysis told me I should not be doing that." The strict regimen of sleep and rest at home was re-implemented in full force by Drew's parents, who understood the gravity of the injuries their son had sustained. "I was reading at a fourth-grade level after that third concussion," Drew remembered, visibly shaken by this recollection. "I still need to reread things sometimes."

Being forced out of a sport due to head injuries is a common theme, especially in youth and high school level high-contact sports such as hockey and football. Unlike other injuries, head injuries cannot be treated as directly, and rest tends to be the most commonly prescribed therapy. As a result, it is harder for an athlete to cope with the trauma from repeated head injuries. And at the youth and high school levels, it is hardly ever worth the risk.

As Drew pushed through his concussion symptoms in the most important academic years of his high school career, he also mailed out an application to Georgetown University. Despite all the literal and figurative headaches of the past few years, Drew refused to lose sight of this dream. And sure enough, on December 15, he got a letter in the mail telling him that this dream was about to become a reality. Despite offers to play Division I hockey from multiple high-ranking programs, Drew chose the Hoyas over hockey.

Halfway across the country, in Long Island, New York, a similar dream was fulfilled as I opened my acceptance letter. Within a few days, Drew and I met via an accepted students' group on Facebook. Little did I know, this random guy from Ohio who I met over the internet before our freshman year would grow to become like a brother to me. And over the course of our college journey, replete with new challenges, we continued to push each other not only in the classroom, but in the gym as well.

On one of our walks over to Yates, Drew recalled the last time he played organized hockey. "After my senior year, a local minor league hockey team in my area had their playoffs coming up, and they had suffered a lot of injuries and did not have enough players to fill out their roster. They called me up one day, and since I was not planning on playing in college, I didn't have to worry about eligibility. So I just practiced with the team. It was pretty insubstantial."

"So, you're telling me you have played professional sports before," I replied, my mouth hanging open in utter disbelief.

"Well I rode the bench most of the time," replied Drew modestly.

"Still, that's crazy. You played professional sports." I still couldn't believe it. This guy with no jump shot I was doing my lab reports next to had played minor league hockey.

"Yeah I guess it was pretty cool. Now check it up moron."

As I bounced Drew the basketball and put a hand in his face, two things became clear. My roommate and best friend was an incredible athlete, and if it weren't for the intervention of his high school training staff and his parents, he might not have bounced back from his concussions to be a star athlete and sharp student. And no matter how tough college seemed to get and no matter how hard Drew worked or how much he improved, he would never beat me at basketball.

CHAPTER 14

THE FEAR FACTOR: HEAD INJURIES IN SOCCER

"Spraining an ankle, sometimes you'll have a season ending injury. From a musculoskeletal standpoint, we know how to take care of those pretty well. Getting dinged in the head? We're still doing a lot of research on that," declares Dr. James Andry, an orthopedic surgeon based out of Phoenix, Arizona. Although the perils associated with repeated brain trauma and concussions have been well-documented and are in the forefront of the public eye in full-contact sports like American football, the massive impact of head injuries in another type of football, soccer, have flown largely under the radar.

Although soccer is viewed as a moderate-contact sport, soccer players are among the most elite athletes in the world and they are capable of inflicting massive amounts of damage on each other. According to Dr. Andry, "These guys run almost a marathon a game, and they can run at almost 20 to 22 miles per hour, which is Olympic-level speed. The amount of energy that they can generate when they drill each other — I'm surprised you don't hear about more deaths or cases of brain bleeds on the field. Their training for sustaining collisions and learning how to tackle is much better than what you see in the NFL."

Although soccer players have garnered a worldwide reputation as athletes who fake injuries to get a favorable call from the referee, they are also among the most competitive athletes on the planet. "They will try to trick you into letting them back on the field early," says Dr. Andry. "I know one athlete that lost consciousness momentarily, and after five to 10 minutes, on the sideline, we asked him, 'are you good to go back out and play,' and he said 'yes,' but when we tested him neurologically, there was no possible way he was going to be cleared."

According to Dr. Andry, "these soccer guys want to stay on the field no matter what, and that is where you have to protect the players from themselves." "You have to evaluate what they're saying versus [the symptoms] they're presenting," explains Dr. Andry. "The physical exam you have can be time-stamped, and it sets a mark for how they are doing. In

15 minutes, if they don't clear the protocol, you have to steal their cleats and hide them from them so they can't get back out there." According to Dr. Andry, the evolution of head injury care in Major League Soccer is improving as a cascade effect of head injuries in the NFL being in the limelight. On the other hand, in Europe, Dr. Andry asserts that "FIFA, I think, is still trying to hide a lot. They don't want Messi missing any games because he's on a concussion protocol."

Working with professional athletes presents a unique challenge because athletes rely on sports as their primary source of income. For doctors, according to Dr. Andry, this often entails producing customized rehabilitation and recovery protocols that allow for an early return to high-level athletic performance. "You pull them out but sometimes you let them go back sooner than you are comfortable with, but it's because they are trying to maintain a living," explains Dr. Andry. "There is ongoing maintenance during the soccer season, and then you definitely take care of them during the off-season." The most common drastic injuries seen on the field are concussions, but most injuries are maintenance issues caused by continuous use. During the season, Dr. Andry claims that the mental battle that accompanies the physical battle is just as significant. "You give them the best possible treatment and deliver it in a way that doesn't devastate them mentally and allows them to get back to training. You have to guide them in terms of how to recover."

Dr. Andry's secret to treating up and coming athletes? Fear. "I try to scare these guys as much as I can to make sure they do what I say to do. Young, active men are generally untrustworthy. Fear is a very good motivator, especially when there is a financial fear or the fear of losing a professional career."

CHAPTER 15

THE CALLING: DR. CHRISTIAN PEAN

———

"I think it's really inspiring and important to get people back to that elite level of function. But I'm also interested in people functioning just fine and going about their daily activities, like going to work and being able to play with their kids," says Dr. Christian Pean, a resident orthopedic surgeon at New York University Langone Health. Although superstar athletes often get a vast majority of the attention when it comes to sports medicine, medicine at its crux is all about patient care. The gravity of sports medicine is massive, regardless of whether the patient is a professional MVP contender or a weekend warrior looking to get back into recreation league games.

"Bones take months to heal," says Dr. Pean. "So that means you don't see these patients in just the operating room. You see them go from having a limb that they could never see themselves walking on again to running again and jogging up a hill to work." Being able to observe patients improve as they bounce back from injuries over a longitudinal period of time is something that sets orthopedics apart from other medical specialties. The power of orthopedics, according to Dr. Pean, is being able to prevent major invasive surgeries. "You would think surgery is this general thing where you have an anatomical issue and you address it and it is the same for everyone, but in reality, you see that that's not the case. In treating high-level athletes, you really have to discuss the risks and benefits as well as their goals. You would have different restrictions on someone who is just trying to get back to walking compared to someone who is trying to one day be a professional quarterback." Dr. Pean explains, "The athlete is unique because they are not just trying to maintain their function. They are trying to achieve a level of performance that is above and beyond what the average person is looking to accomplish."

The role of sports medicine, and medicine as a whole, is to produce positive health outcomes in a system that revolves around patient care. A major responsibility of physicians, as Dr. Pean asserts, is to make an impact beyond working on individual patients. Dr. Pean has committed himself to working to produce structural change that improves access to medicine for underprivileged populations. A good doctor always has a finger on the pulse of policy. According to Dr. Pean, "Medicine and science are platforms for social change. We cannot let fear dictate the choices we make." And whether the patient is a superstar professional athlete making millions of dollars a year or a parent looking to stay casually active with their children, it is the role of physicians to serve as advocates for patients and to call out inequalities to health care access and quality treatment. "Our job is to keep people safe, but in sports, people put themselves in risk," says Dr. Pean. "You go from being a layperson to being in charge of someone's career. Limb. Life. The process of understanding the gravity of your role is something really unique."

As Dr. Pean puts it, "Medicine is not a job. It's a calling."

CONCLUSION

WINNING

"Real health is achieved by putting in work," asserts Dr. Kyle F. Worell, a chiropractor and spinal care specialist based out of Manhattan. "The future of health care lies in the use of technology and connecting with and coaching people." One thing about the intersection of sports and medicine is clear: There is an immense amount of effort being put in by both physicians and athletes. There is work being put in both on and off the field by both groups of people. Dr. Worell explains that sports are highly repetitive: "Most of injury comes from the repetition being the wrong way: too much, too soon, too fast, too hard."

Caring for athletes presents unique issues, as they push their bodies to the extreme limits of human capabilities. And when they get hurt, it is not always easy to judge how bad the injury is unless it is immobilizing. According to Dr. Bryan Whitfield, an orthopedic surgeon at Emory Orthopedics, "It's not like we have MRIs on the field, so we have to make our best judgment. Certainly, if it's borderline, I am going to err on the side of being safe, and sometimes that is frustrating for the parents, the coach, and the player. But the worst thing I can do is let you get hurt worse."

According to Dr. Christine Ellie, a Doctor of Podiatric Medicine and an expert on foot and ankle injuries, "Using 100% of something that is at 100% anatomically is ideal." Dr. Ellie stresses the importance of being aware of an athlete's precise medical condition before clearing them to play. "My job is not to keep someone in the sport if they're hurt," explains Dr. Ellie. Oftentimes, at the youth sports level, that entails fighting off pressure from parents, coaches, and athletes themselves. This message is resonated by many other leaders in the field of sports medicine, such as Dr. Michael Day, an orthopedic surgeon at Summit Health Group. According to Dr. Day, "Ultimately, there should not be a different set of ethics, because they are a patient first and an athlete second. The risk-to-benefit discussion may be different if they are talking about the timing of a surgery or how it is going to fit into the season. You have to do what is in their best interest. If they are getting paid for their sport, that is something that they take into consideration."

Part of what makes sports medicine such a special and unique field is the approach taken by physicians. Dr. Holly Beach, a sports medicine physician and preventative medicine specialist based in Arizona, asserts, "My approach is the same: ordinary folks get the best treatment." According to world-renowned orthopedic surgeon Dr. James Andrews, "Motivation comes in all packages. Some of the weekend warriors that love their recreation can be as motivated as anybody. If you're not motivated, you're not going to be an athlete in the first place. Sports medicine is so popular because your patients are relatively easy to take care of."

When dealing with athletics at the professional level, there is a lot at stake. According to Dr. Roger Härtl, the director of spinal surgery and neurotrauma at Weill Cornell Brain and Spine Center and the head neurosurgeon for the New York Giants, "I'm impressed with how seriously players take injuries." Given the publicity being received by the dangers associated with football, changes have been made to the NFL's concussion protocol. As explained by Dr. Härtl, "In general, now, the threshold to diagnose a concussion is very low, so we diagnose it more frequently now than in the past." Unfortunately, even at the professional level, according to Dr. Whitfield, "We still have a lot of limitations in what we can do. We still don't know how to accelerate biology. It is not uncommon that the pain goes away, but if the patient goes back to their sport too early, they are likely to get reinjured."

According to Dr. Whitfield, complications and imperfections are a part of the outcomes associated with sports medicine and major injuries. "Do we get it right 100% of the time? No. Do complications and other things happen during the course of treatment? Absolutely. After you perform surgery, does it ever make someone perfect? It doesn't seem to. We have to do what we think is best for the patient, but it does not work out every time." As a result, Dr. Whitfield and countless other orthopedic surgeons and sports medicine specialists are hoping to see an improvement in preventative medicine moving forward. According to Dr. Day, "Pro athletes are superhuman because people work on them every day." And although delivering the best possible health outcomes is supremely important, as Dr. James Andrews says, "Don't let anybody tell you that winning is not important."

ACKNOWLEDGEMENTS

—

First and foremost, thank you to my amazing parents, Parul Dave and Rajesh Dave. You always make me feel like I can do anything I put my mind to, and you are there every step of the way in all of my endeavors to celebrate when I succeed and to pick me up when I do not. I owe it all to you. I love you so much and am blessed to have you as my parents.

A huge thank you to Ansh Desai, Milan Shah, Nisarg Patel, Raj Shah, Ajay Singh, Nihar Shah, Brandon Gosine, Ashwin Palaniappan, and Ayush Goel. You always push me to be a better version of myself, and you are more than brothers to me. I am so excited to see all that we do in the years to come. Also, this book immortalizes Banana Swirl/Aftermath.

Thank you to my Georgetown friends, especially Luc Nikiema, Shrayus Sortur, Raghav Ranga, and Drew Musgrave. I cannot begin to imagine my Georgetown experience without all of you and being able to live with you and spend time with you has made these past three years among the best in my life.

Thank you to my amazing family: Jay Dave, Rahulkumar Dave, Jayshree Dave, Kartik Dave, Gita Dave, Dipak Dave, Sapna Pattni, Krunal Pattni, Dev Patni, Urmila Pandya, Uday Trivedi, Sujata Trivedi, Suchi Trivedi, Niti Trivedi, Kirtikumar Pandya, Malti Pandya, Amit Pandya, Hemina Pandya, Poojan Pandya, Anushka Pandya, Parag Pandya, Ami Pandya, Aashka Pandya, Ishaan Pandya, Hemang Trivedi, Aarti Trivedi, and Niral Shah. I am so thankful to be able to learn from you and to be surrounded by so much love.

Thank you to all the amazing people who took the time to be interviewed for this book. I learned so much about the world of medicine and sports from you and being able to speak with you has further fueled my drive to one day become a physician. Thank you, Ivan Tchatchouwo, for the continuous support and for discussing everything with me from rap music to sports training techniques to the direction of this book. Thank you, Dr. James Andrews, for making a childhood dream of mine come true by spending fifteen minutes talking to me about not only your own medical career but my future medical career.

A special thank you to Dr. Christian Pean, Dr. Christopher Dodson, and Dr. Michael Day for going above and beyond answering a few questions about orthopedic surgery and sports medicine and serving as mentors to me. I cannot wait to one day become a physician myself, and I am honored to continue to have your guidance along this journey.

Thank you to my Herricks friends, especially Michael Procops, Priyanka Kumar, and Emanuel Alyaszadeh. I really appreciate the support, and I hope you enjoyed the book.

Thank you to Eric Koester, Barbara Hightower, and my publishing team at New Degree Press. You took me from a wide-eyed college student with a cool idea to a published author with a book in my hands.

A special thank you to my other backers: Harsh Ray, Jigisha Ray, Nitin Ray, Dhruv Ray, Mohini Bodawala, Penny Simon, Wilbert Staten, Steven Grube, Piyush Parikh, Amita Parikh, Nina Mehta, Samirkumar Shukla, Hasmukh Patel, Tariq Muhammad, Vicky Khanna, Rajendra Shah, and Glaucia Goncalves. Publishing this book would not have been possible without you.

WORKS CITED

CHAPTER 1

Curry, Stephen, and Neymar Jr. "The Crossover." The Players' Tribune. Last modified October 30, 2018. Accessed May 29, 2019. https://www.theplayerstribune.com/en-us/articles/the-crossover-stephen-curry-neymar-jr.

"THE GAME Steph Curry BECAME a LEGEND 2016.02.27 at Thunder - 46 Pts, 12 3's, CLUTCH!" Video file. YouTube. Posted by FreeDawkins, February 27, 2016. Accessed May 29, 2019. https://www.youtube.com/watch?v=quI--kovXgI.

"NBA League Averages - Per Game." Basketball Reference. Last modified 2019. Accessed May 29, 2019. https://www.basketball-reference.com/leagues/NBA_stats_per_game.html.

Schwartz, Nick. "Steph Curry reflects on what draft experts said about him in 2009." FTW! Last modified January 9, 2019. https://ftw.usatoday.com/2019/01/steph-curry-draft-criticism-warriors.

"Stephen Curry." Basketball Reference. Last modified 2019. Accessed May 29, 2019. https://www.basketball-reference.com/players/c/currysto1.html.

Torre, Pablo S. "How Stephen Curry got the best worst ankles in sports play." ESPN. Last modified February 10, 2016. Accessed

May 29, 2019. http://www.espn.com/nba/story/_/id/14750602/
how-golden-state-warriors-stephen-curry-got-best-worst-ankles-sports.

"Warriors Guard Stephen Curry Undergoes Successful Surgery on Right Ankle."
NBA.com. Last modified May 25, 2011. Accessed May 29, 2019. https://www.nba.
com/warriors/news/curry_ankle_surgery_052511.html.

CHAPTER 2

Bieler, Des. "Kevin Durant: Finals game-winner felt like LeBron James 'passing
the torch' to him." The Washington Post. Last modified November 16, 2017.
Accessed May 30, 2019. https://www.washingtonpost.com/news/early-lead/
wp/2017/11/16/kevin-durant-finals-game-winner-felt-like-lebron-james-pas-
sing-the-torch-to-him/?utm_term=.a91a67e9171b.

ESPN. "Why Kevin Durant sees world differently now." Hospital for Special
Surgery. Last modified June 1, 2017. Accessed May 30, 2019. https://www.hss.
edu/newsroom_espn-kevin-durant-nba-playoffs.asp.

ESPN.com News Services. "Kevin Durant Fractures Foot." ABC News. Last
modified October 12, 2014. Accessed May 30, 2019. https://abcnews.go.com/
Sports/kevin-durant-fractures-foot/story?id=26138491.

Gitlin, Marty. "Videos show Thunder star Kevin Durant accelerating rehab." CBS Sports. Last modified June 26, 2015.
Accessed May 30, 2019. https://www.cbssports.com/nba/news/
videos-show-thunder-star-kevin-durant-accelerating-rehab/.

MacMullan, Jackie. "Why Kevin Durant sees world differently now." ESPN. Last modified June 1, 2017. Accessed May 30,
2019. http://www.espn.com/nba/story/_/page/presents-19505704/
nba-playoffs-why-kevin-durant-sees-world-differently-now.

Mayberry, Darnell. "Kevin Durant undergoes second surgery on right foot, will
be reevaluated in one week." The Oklahoman. Last modified February 23, 2015.
Accessed May 30, 2019. https://oklahoman.com/article/5395690/kevin-durant-
undergoes-second-surgery-on-right-foot-will-be-reevaluated-in-one-week.

"Mini-Movie: NBA Finals 2017 Game 3 | Warriors Win Thriller in Cleveland."
Video file. YouTube. Posted by NBA, June 8, 2017. Accessed May 30, 2019.
https://www.youtube.com/watch?v=xO21McAgIP0.

Sherman, J. A. "Kevin Durant's foot injury and recovery: ortho-paedic surgeon Dr. David Geier offers dispassionate analysis." Welcome to Loud City. Last modified October 13, 2014. Accessed May 30, 2019. https://www.welcometoloudcity.com/2014/10/13/6968383/kevin-durant-thunder-foot-jones-fracture-doctor-david-geier.

Young, Royce. "Kevin Durant expects to be fully cleared by August." ESPN. Last modified July 4, 2015. Accessed May 30, 2019. http://www.espn.com/nba/story/_/id/13199049/kevin-durant-oklahoma-city-thunder-tries-move-forward-season-ending-injury.

———. "Kevin Durant: Foot not a concern." ESPN. Last modified December 10, 2014. Accessed May 30, 2019. http://www.espn.com.au/nba/story/_/id/12010575/kevin-durant-oklahoma-city-thunder-not-worried-surgically-repaired-right-foot.

———. "Kevin Durant Fractures Foot." ESPN. Last modified October 13, 2014. Accessed May 30, 2019. http://www.espn.com/nba/story/_/id/11688088/kevin-durant-oklahoma-city-thunder-fractured-foot.

CHAPTER 3

"All-Time Leaders: Career Triple-Doubles." NBA.com. Last modified December 28, 2016. Accessed May 31, 2019. https://stats.nba.com/articles/all-time-leaders-career-triple-doubles/.

Conway, Tyler. "Timeline of Russell Westbrook's Journey from Knee Injury to NBA Return." Bleacher Report. Last modified November 3, 2013. Accessed May 31, 2019. https://bleacherreport.com/articles/1816655-timeline-of-russell-westbrooks-journey-from-knee-injury-to-nba-return.

"Postgame Russell Westbrook Interview 42nd Triple Double! | April 9, 2017." Video file. YouTube. Posted by NBA Highlights, April 9, 2017. Accessed May 31, 2019. https://www.youtube.com/watch?v=56yjR8mTT6M.

"Russell Westbrook." ESPN. Last modified 2019. Accessed May 31, 2019. http://www.espn.com/nba/player/gamelog/_/id/3468/year/2017/russell-westbrook.

"Russell Westbrook Full KIA MVP Presentation & Speech | NBA Awards 2017." Video file. YouTube. Posted by NBA, June 26, 2017. Accessed May 31, 2019. https://www.youtube.com/watch?v=vEg-jp8vkT4.

"Russell Westbrook NBA RECORD 42ND TRIPLE DOUBLE Full Game Highlights | April 9, 2017." Video file. YouTube. Posted by NBA, April 9, 2017. Accessed May 31, 2019. https://www.youtube.com/watch?v=sLwLoicdKsI.

"Westbrook speaks on injury, expected on crutches 4-5 weeks." NBA.com. Last modified May 9, 2013. Accessed May 31, 2019. https://www.nba.com/2013/news/05/09/westbrook-discusses-injury/.

Winfield, Kristian. "A history of Russell Westbrook's many knee surgeries." SB Nation. Last modified September 12, 2018. Accessed May 31, 2019. https://www.sbnation.com/2018/9/12/17851948/russell-westbrook-knee-injury-surgery-history-thunder.

Wojnarowski, Adrian. "Russell Westbrook returning to Thunder lineup against Suns." Yahoo! Sports. Last modified November 3, 2013. Accessed May 31, 2019. https://ca.sports.yahoo.com/news/nba--russell-westbrook-could-return-to-thunder-lineup-within-two-weeks-003220954.html.

CHAPTER 4

Amick, Sam. "Paul George recovering from surgery for fracture." USA Today. Last modified August 2, 2014. Accessed May 31, 2019. https://www.usatoday.com/story/sports/nba/pacers/2014/08/02/paul-george-surgery-compound-fracture-tibia-fibula-team-usa/13505781/.

B/R Studios. "Paul George's Road Back: Reliving the Nightmare Ep. 1." Bleacher Report. Accessed May 31, 2019. https://bleacherreport.com/articles/2344193-paul-georges-road-back-reliving-the-nightmare-ep-1.

Duffy, Thomas. "The doctor and the superstar." Nets Daily. Last modified April 6, 2015. Accessed May 31, 2019. https://www.netsdaily.com/2015/4/6/8322857/will-paul-george-kill-the-nets-playoff-chances.

Gatto, Tom. "Paul George suffers broken leg during Team USA scrimmage." Sporting News. Last modified August 1, 2014. Accessed May 31, 2019. https://www.sportingnews.com/us/other-sports/news/paul-george-gruesome-injury-team-usa-fiba-world-cup-pacers/1bmm64ta9bo8m1mm4lfq15ukun.

NBA Highlights. "Paul George breaks his leg... - Team USA - Blue vs White 2014." YouTube. Last modified August 1, 2014. Accessed May 31, 2019. https://www.youtube.com/watch?v=Fi2RoIlCXlA.

Newport, Kyle. "Paul George Is Dunking in Practice 6 Months After Gruesome Leg Injury." Bleacher Report. Last modified January 15, 2015. Accessed May 31, 2019. https://bleacherreport.com/articles/2331388-paul-george-is-dunking-in-practice-6-months-after-gruesome-leg-injury.

"Paul George." Spotrac. Last modified 2019. Accessed May 31, 2019. https://www.spotrac.com/nba/oklahoma-city-thunder/paul-george-6892/.

"Paul George's return after broken leg + first points! (04.05.2015)." Video file. YouTube. Posted by NBAHighlights2, April 5, 2015. https://www.youtube.com/watch?v=9uPND2JKKSI.

"Paul George The Road Back The Lost Season? Episode 3." Video file. YouTube. Posted by Ball_Motivation, March 20, 2015. Accessed May 31, 2019. https://www.youtube.com/watch?v=7d3NaNnThaw.

Powell, Shaun. "For Pacers' leading man, comeback has been completed." NBA.com. Last modified February 8, 2016. Accessed May 31, 2019. https://www.nba.com/2016/news/features/shaun_powell/02/08/paul-george-all-the-way-back-to-all-star-level/.

"Russell Westbrook House Party Where Paul George Return | Behind-The-Scenes." Video file. YouTube. Posted July 7, 2018. Accessed May 31, 2019. https://www.youtube.com/watch?v=-S2O5FR0Wk8.

CHAPTER 5

Bryant, Kobe. *Facebook* (blog). Entry posted April 13, 2013. Accessed May 31, 2019. https://www.facebook.com/kobe/posts/this-is-such-bs-all-the-training-and-sacrifice-just-flew-out-the-window-with-one/10151563315250419/.

"Career Highlights." Mamba Out. Accessed May 31, 2019. http://mambaout.com/achievements.html.

Ding, Kevin. "Kobe Bryant's Maniacal Ambition a Challenge to His Aging Body." Bleacher Report. Last modified October 4, 2013. Accessed May 31, 2019. https://bleacherreport.com/articles/1798900-kobe-bryants-maniacal-ambition-a-challenge-to-his-aging-body.

Farmer, Sam. "Exclusive: Doctor who performed Kobe Bryant's surgery is optimistic." Los Angeles Times. Last modified April 14, 2013. Accessed May 31, 2019. https://www.latimes.com/sports/lakers/la-xpm-2013-apr-14-la-sp-ln-kobe-bryant-achilles-surgery-20130414-story.html.

Kay, Alex. "Breaking Down the Steps of Kobe Bryant's Return from Achilles Tear." Bleacher Report. Last modified December 8, 2013. Accessed May 31, 2019. https://bleacherreport.com/articles/1780056-breaking-down-the-steps-of-kobe-bryants-return-from-achilles-tear.

"Kobe Bryant 'Control What You Can Control' Achilles Recovery Inspirational." Video file. YouTube. Posted by NBA Highlights Nonstop, May 26, 2015. Accessed May 31, 2019. https://www.youtube.com/watch?v=LxvrOE4-J8s.

"Kobe Bryant final game fourth quarter only shots." Video file. YouTube. Posted by Marc S, April 17, 2016. Accessed May 31, 2019. https://www.youtube.com/watch?v=KjvUxW6NoRA.

"Kobe Bryant's Final Game Farewell Speech." Video file. YouTube. Posted by Mr. Mafeeny Chuggart, April 13, 2016. Accessed May 31, 2019. https://www.youtube.com/watch?v=pOHQWCqNV9E.

"Kobe Bryant s torn achilles + shoots freethrows_medium." Video file. YouTube. Posted by Celse Dav, April 26, 2013. Accessed May 31, 2019. https://www.youtube.com/watch?v=g2afNT_7c90.

Murphy, David. "Timeline of Kobe Bryant's Return from Devastating Achilles Injury." Bleacher Report. Last modified December 6, 2013. Accessed May 31, 2019. https://bleacherreport.com/articles/1856278-timeline-of-kobe-bryants-return-from-devastating-achilles-injury.

Onslow, Justin. "Kobe Bryant Targets 2013 Season Opener for Return from Achilles Tear." Bleacher Report. Last modified June 3, 2013. Accessed May 31, 2019. https://bleacherreport.com/articles/1660861-kobe-bryant-targets-opening-night-of-next-season-to-return-from-achilles-tear.

Pincus, Eric. "Kobe Bryant says he 'shattered' Achilles recovery timetable." Los Angeles Times. Last modified August 5, 2013. Accessed May 31, 2019. https://www.latimes.com/sports/lakers/la-xpm-2013-aug-05-la-sp-ln-kobe-bryant-achilles-20130805-story.html.

"Utah Jazz at Los Angeles Lakers Play-By-Play, April 13, 2016." Basketball Reference. Accessed May 31, 2019. https://www.basketball-reference.com/boxscores/pbp/201604130LAL.html.

CHAPTER 6

"Cleveland Cavaliers at Golden State Warriors Box Score, June 2, 2016." Basketball Reference. Last modified 2019. Accessed May 31, 2019. https://www.basketball-reference.com/boxscores/201606020GSW.html.

Coro, Paul. "Shaun Livingston's career nearly ended with a grotesque knee injury. Instead he's a two-time NBA champion seeking another title." Los Angeles Times. Last modified April 13, 2018. Accessed May 31, 2019. https://www.latimes.com/sports/nba/la-sp-nba-playoffs-livingston-20180413-story.html.

SLAM Magazine. *Ready or Not … Here They Come.* Image. Accessed May 31, 2019. https://vignette.wikia.nocookie.net/slammagazine/images/b/b7/SLAM80.jpg/revision/latest?cb=20130203072929.

Spears, Marc J. "Can't Be Defeated: The Shaun Livingston Story." The Undefeated. Last modified May 17, 2016. Accessed May 31, 2019. https://theundefeated.com/features/never-defeated-the-shaun-livingston-story/.

"WORST NBA Injury EVER? Doctor Explains Shaun Livingston Injury." Video file. YouTube. Posted by Brian Sutterer, December 22, 2018. Accessed May 31, 2019. https://www.youtube.com/watch?v=Et4Nqu3vAtg.

Zillgitt, Jeff. "How Shaun Livingston found NBA life after ugly injury." USA Today. Last modified March 20, 2014. Accessed May 31, 2019. https://www.usatoday.com/story/sports/nba/nets/2014/03/20/shaun-livingston-return-knee-injury-brooklyn/6655413/.

CHAPTER 7

Berger, Ken. "How trainer gets spent LeBron James from one Herculean effort to next." CBS Sports. Last modified June 10, 2015. Accessed May 31, 2019. https://www.cbssports.com/nba/news/how-trainer-gets-spent-lebron-james-from-one-herculean-effort-to-next/.

Bishara, Motez. "LeBron James: Keeping a billion-dollar body in shape." CNN. Last modified December 13, 2017. Accessed May 31, 2019. https://www.cnn.com/2017/12/13/sport/lebron-james-physical-trainer-mike-mancias-cleveland-cavs/index.html.

Cassilo, David. "What's the Secret to LeBron James' Athletic Invincibility?" Bleacher Report. Last modified October 10, 2016. Accessed May 31, 2019. https://bleacherreport.com/articles/2661150-whats-the-secret-to-lebron-james-athletic-invincibility.

"Cleveland Cavaliers at Golden State Warriors Box Score, June 13, 2016." Basketball Reference. Last modified 2019. Accessed May 31, 2019. https://www.basketball-reference.com/boxscores/201606130GSW.html.

Davis, Scott. "LeBron James takes immaculate care of his body, and the NBA world is in awe of it." Business Insider. Last modified June 3, 2018. Accessed May 31, 2019. https://www.businessinsider.com/lebron-james-body-care-workouts-diet-insane-2017-10.

Estiler, Keith. "18-Year-Old LeBron James Predicts Future Success in Latest Nike Video." Hypebeast. Last modified October 21, 2018. Accessed May 31, 2019. https://hypebeast.com/2018/10/lebron-james-nike-just-do-it-film.

Florjancic, Matthew. "'I'm coming home': Revisit LeBron James' infamous letter." WKYC3. Last modified June 20, 2016. Accessed May 31, 2019. https://www.wkyc.com/article/sports/nba/cavaliers/im-coming-home-revisit-lebron-james-infamous-letter/250422956.

"Golden State Warriors at Cleveland Cavaliers Box Score, June 16, 2016." Basketball Reference. Last modified 2019. Accessed May 31, 2019. https://www.basketball-reference.com/boxscores/201606160CLE.html.

Gonzalez, Eddie. "LeBron's Legendary Block Is Somehow Even Better When Told From Richard Jefferson's Point Of View." Uproxx. Last modified March 23, 2017. Accessed May 31, 2019. https://uproxx.com/dimemag/lebron-block-finals-richard-jefferson-retelling-podcast-video/.

Gundersen, Erik García. "Two staff members with strong LeBron ties have left the Cavaliers." LeBronWire. Last modified July 20, 2018. Accessed May 31, 2019. https://lebronwire.usatoday.com/2018/07/20/two-staff-members-with-strong-lebron-ties-have-left-the-cavaliers/.

"LeBron James' Historic Block on Andre Iguodala From All Angles." Video file. YouTube. Posted by NBA, June 21, 2016. Accessed May 31, 2019. https://www.youtube.com/watch?v=-zd62MxKXp8.

"Michael Jordan." ESPN. Last modified 2019. Accessed May 31, 2019. http://www.espn.com/nba/player/stats/_/id/1035/michael-jordan.

NBA. "LeBron James." NBA Advanced Stats. Last modified 2019. Accessed May 31, 2019. https://stats.nba.com/player/2544/.

"NBA MVP Award Winners." NBA. Last modified 2019. Accessed May 31, 2019. http://www.nba.com/history/awards/mvp.

NBC Sports. "LeBron: 'Cleveland this is for you.'" Video file. NBC Sports Philadelphia. Accessed May 31, 2019. https://www.nbcsports.com/philadelphia/video/lebron-james-cleveland-you.

Simmons, Bill. "LeBron James's Life Is Constructed to Keep Him on the Court." The Ringer. Last modified June 8, 2016. Accessed May 31, 2019. https://www.theringer.com/2016/6/8/16040612/nba-lebron-james-bill-simmons-malcolm-gladwell-5369d6959c67.

Stotts, Jeff. "An In-Depth Look at the Injury History of LeBron James." In Street Clothes. Last modified January 1, 2015. Accessed May 31, 2019. http://instreetclothes.com/2015/01/01/depth-look-injury-history-lebron-james/.

"2017-2018 NBA Season Leaders." ESPN. Last modified 2019. Accessed May 31, 2019. http://www.espn.com/nba/seasonleaders/_/league/nba/sort/avgMinutes/year/2018.

"2002 LeBron James Sports Illustrated First Issue No Label." Bonanza. Accessed May 31, 2019. https://www.bonanza.com/listings/2002-Lebron-James-Sports-Illustrated-First-Issue-No-Label/659844193?goog_pla=1&gpid=293946777986&keyword=&goog_pla=1&pos=104&ad_type=pla&gclid=CjwKCAiA3vfgBRB9EiwAkfpd3D9gaMCc97nc6ZRbsFQOQ78vV59TxJ4NRoVohsE6DifJtcU5k6iChhoCUYcQAvD_BwE.

Windhorst, Brian. "How LeBron James fixed his back and is on track to play all 82 games." ESPN. Last modified March 19, 2018. Accessed May 31, 2019. http://www.espn.com/nba/story/_/id/22778062/how-lebron-james-fixed-back-track-play-all-82-games-nba.

CHAPTER 8

"Adrian Peterson." Pro Football Reference. Last modified 2019. Accessed May 31, 2019. https://www.pro-football-reference.com/players/P/PeteAd01/gamelog/2012/.

"Adrian Peterson goes for Eric Dickerson's rushing record - 2012 Week 17 Vikings vs. Packers." Video file. YouTube. Posted by NFL, July 21, 2015. Accessed May 31, 2019. https://www.youtube.com/watch?v=WVkEIydlmFA.

"Adrian Peterson's rapid recovery with HydroWorx pools." Video file. YouTube. Posted by HydroWorx International Inc., September 19, 2008. Accessed May 31, 2019. https://www.youtube.com/watch?v=k_40Rh984bI.

"Adrian Peterson's recovery aided by ERMI Inc." Video file. YouTube. Posted by ERMI Inc, December 11, 2012. Accessed May 31, 2019. https://www.youtube.com/watch?v=YAI2oFqF_38&t=1s.

"Adrian Peterson: Torn ACL was the worst pain ever." Video file. YouTube. Posted by Graham Bensinger, September 7, 2016. Accessed May 31, 2019. https://www.youtube.com/watch?v=JrdlxFY26cc&t=14s.

"NFL: Peterson's road to recovery." Video file. YouTube. Posted by Espnamerica, May 20, 2012. Accessed May 31, 2019. https://www.youtube.com/watch?v=RCxPkvD-Y88.

"#1 Adrian Peterson: Torn ACL to Rushing for Over 2,000 yards | Top 10 Player Comebacks | NFL Films." Video file. YouTube. Posted by NFL Films, November 4, 2016. Accessed May 31, 2019. https://www.youtube.com/watch?v=ZWSYojBe7yY.

Pioneer Press. "Adrian Peterson's surgeon, James Andrews, says Vikings back 'has defied all odds.'" Twin Cities Pioneer Press. Last modified January 3, 2013. Accessed May 31, 2019. https://www.twincities.com/2013/01/03/adrian-petersons-surgeon-james-andrews-says-vikings-back-has-defied-all-odds/.

Welch, Hanuman. "Minnesota Vikings' Adrian Peterson Uses Nintendo Wii for His Physical Therapy." Complex. Last modified August 12, 2012. Accessed May 31, 2019. https://www.complex.com/pop-culture/2012/08/minnesota-vikings-adrian-peterson-incorporates-wii-into-his-physical-therapy-regimen.

Wilson, Ryan. "Dr. Andrews on Adrian Peterson's recovery: 'He has defied the odds.'" CBS Sports. Last modified January 4, 2013. Accessed May 31, 2019. https://www.cbssports.com/nfl/news/dr-andrews-on-adrian-petersons-recovery-he-has-defied-the-odds/.

CHAPTER 9

Dator, James. "Here's a list of every major NFL record Peyton Manning holds." SB Nation. Last modified March 6, 2016. Accessed May 31, 2019. https://www.sbnation.com/nfl/2014/10/19/7010081/peyton-manning-nfl-record-list-most-touchdowns-509.

"#4: Broncos vs. Chiefs (Week 2) | Top 20 Games of 2015 | NFL." Video file. YouTube. Posted by NFL, September 17, 2015. Accessed May 31, 2019. https://www.youtube.com/watch?v=Mt2u8TIKRCA.

Jenkins, Sally. "Peyton Manning on his neck surgeries rehab — and how he almost didn't make it back." The Washington Post. Last modified October 21, 2013. Accessed May 31, 2019. https://www.washingtonpost.com/sports/redskins/peyton-manning-on-his-neck-surgeries-rehab--and-how-he-almost-didnt-make-it-back/2013/10/21/8e3b5ca6-3a55-11e3-b7ba-503fb5822c3e_story.html?noredirect=on&utm_term=.7d30e8dca503.

Nathan, Alec. "Peyton Manning Informs Broncos He Will Retire." Bleacher Report. Last modified March 6, 2016. Accessed May 31, 2019. https://bleacherreport.com/articles/2568778-peyton-manning-reportedly-will-announce-retirement.

"Peyton Manning." NFL. Last modified 2019. Accessed May 31, 2019. http://www.nfl.com/player/peytonmanning/2501863/careerstats.

Vaccaro, Alexander, and Gregory Schroeder. "Interest growing in Peyton Manning-like neck injuries in the NFL, MLB." Sports Illustrated. Last modified March 27, 2015. Accessed May 31, 2019. https://www.si.com/edge/2015/03/27/peyton-manning-neck-injury-rothman-denver-broncos.

CHAPTER 10

CNN Library. "Hurricane Katrina Statistics Fast Facts." CNN. Last modified August 30, 2018. Accessed May 31, 2019. https://www.cnn.com/2013/08/23/us/hurricane-katrina-statistics-fast-facts/index.html.

"Divisional Round - Arizona Cardinals at New Orleans Saints - January 16th, 2010." Pro Football Reference. Last modified 2019. Accessed May 31, 2019. https://www.pro-football-reference.com/boxscores/201001160nor.htm.

"drew brees injury + rehab." Video file. YouTube. Posted by Robert Sevier, December 9, 2010. Accessed May 31, 2019. https://www.youtube.com/watch?v=io5pOS8WPIo.

"Drew Brees My Professional Care Story." Video file. YouTube. Posted by PerformanceHealth, August 30, 2017. Accessed May 31, 2019. https://www.youtube.com/watch?v=4ChGRy9TXWw.

Erickson, Joel A. "The story of Drew Brees and the '1-in-500 injury' that couldn't stop his historic career." The New Orleans Advocate. Last modified October 7, 2018. Accessed May 31, 2019. https://www.theadvocate.com/new_orleans/sports/saints/article_abaf4c0a-c805-11e8-9412-2391641ec153.html.

"NFC Championship - Minnesota Vikings at New Orleans Saints - January 24th, 2010." Pro Football Reference. Last modified 2019. Accessed May 31, 2019. https://www.pro-football-reference.com/boxscores/201001240nor.htm.

"'9 for No. 9: A Champion's Journey' | Drew Brees | Ch 4: The Injury." Video file. YouTube. Posted by New Orleans Saints, September 4, 2018. Accessed May 31, 2019. https://www.youtube.com/watch?v=_79b2HUu9js.

"Super Bowl XLIV - New Orleans Saints vs. Indianapolis Colts - February 7th, 2010." Pro Football Reference. Last modified 2019. Accessed May 31, 2019. https://www.pro-football-reference.com/boxscores/201002070clt.htm.

"Super Bowl XLIV: Saints vs. Colts highlights." Video file. YouTube. Posted by NFL, February 6, 2015. Accessed May 31, 2019. https://www.youtube.com/watch?v=PozuCOfcSjc.

"2008 New Orleans Saints Statistics & Players." Pro Football Reference. Last modified 2019. Accessed May 31, 2019. https://www.pro-football-reference.com/teams/nor/2008.htm.

"2009 New Orleans Saints Statistics & Players." Pro Football Reference. Last modified 2019. Accessed May 31, 2019. https://www.pro-football-reference.com/teams/nor/2009.htm.

"2007 New Orleans Saints Statistics & Players." Pro Football Reference. Last modified 2019. Accessed May 31, 2019. https://www.pro-football-reference.com/teams/nor/2007.htm.

"2006 New Orleans Saints Statistics & Players." Pro Football Reference. Last modified 2019. Accessed May 31, 2019. https://www.pro-football-reference.com/teams/nor/2006.htm.

CHAPTER 11

Associated Press. "Giancarlo Stanton: Could be worse." ESPN. Last modified September 19, 2014. Accessed May 31, 2019. http://www.espn.com/mlb/story/_/id/11549652/giancarlo-stanton-miami-marlins-says-recovering-well-facial-injuries.

Frisaro, Joe. "Stanton fishes out close vote, wins NL MVP." MLB.com. Last modified November 16, 2017. Accessed May 31, 2019. https://www.mlb.com/news/marlins-giancarlo-stanton-wins-nl-mvp-award-c262051396.

———. "Stanton upbeat, thankful hit to face wasn't worse." MLB.com. Last modified September 18, 2014. Accessed May 31, 2019. https://www.mlb.com/news/marlins-giancarlo-stanton-upbeat-thankful-hit-to-face-wasnt-worse/c-95316098.

"Giancarlo Stanton Hit in the Face with Pitch - FULL VIDEO." Video file. You-Tube. Posted by G4MarchMadnessHD, September 11, 2014. Accessed May 31, 2019. https://www.youtube.com/watch?v=sBQPk9Bva14.

Martin, Dan. "The only thing that remains from Giancarlo Stanton's moment of terror." New York Post. Last modified March 11, 2018. Accessed May 31, 2019. https://nypost.com/2018/03/11/the-only-thing-that-remains-from-giancarlo-stantons-moment-of-terror/.

Spencer, Clark. "Here's why the Marlins' Giancarlo Stanton may win the MVP — and why he may not." Miami Herald. Last modified November 16, 2017. Accessed May 31, 2019. https://www.miamiherald.com/sports/spt-columns-blogs/fish-bytes/article184964153.html.

Spencer, Clark, and Manny Navarro. "Miami Marlins' Giancarlo Stanton suffers facial fractures, likely won't return this season." Miami Herald. Last modified September 12, 2014. Accessed May 31, 2019. https://www.miamiherald.com/sports/mlb/miami-marlins/article2087465.html.

Made in the USA
Middletown, DE
21 August 2019